POLAR MOLECULES

Peter Josef William

By

P. DEBYE, Ph.D.

*Professor of Physics and Director
of the Physical Institute in the
University of Leipsig, Germany*

DOVER PUBLICATIONS, INC.

Library of Congress Catalog Card Number: 58-13773

Manufactured in the United States of America

Dover Publications, Inc.
180 Varick Street
New York, N. Y. 10014

PREFACE

This book contains a survey of questions treated in connection with the conception of polar molecules as being systems having a distribution of electrical charges which can be characterized by a permanent electric moment. Since the appearance in 1912 of my first article many contributions on the experimental side of the problem have shown that absolute measurement of polarity based on this idea may successfully be used to determine the geometrical arrangement of the atoms in a molecule. On the theoretical side the introduction of the quantum theory in its most modern form has made it possible to develop in detail the connection existing between polarity and the phenomena of dispersion and absorption, especially in the infra-red. An interesting example of the inter-dependence of experiment and theory also resulting from the electrical definition of polarity is exhibited in the field of the electrical saturation phenomena, analogous to ferromagnetism.

The literature on the subject is scattered in journals of many countries and different languages. Apart from my own interest in the subject, this was one of the main reasons which induced me to attempt the writing of this comprehensive monograph. However, I do not think that I would have succeeded in fininishing it if I had not had the encouragement of so many American scientists and friends, including A. H. and K. T. Compton, J. Langmuir, G. N. Lewis, C. E. Mendenhall, R. A. Millikan, A. A. Noyes and G. B. Pegram. I was greatly helped by having opportunities to discuss special parts with J. Errera, Ch. Manneback, H. Sack, R. Sänger, C. P. Smyth, J. W. Williams, and C. T. Zahn, all of whom have made contributions of importance to the subject. In the preparation of the text H. P. Evans of the University of Wisconsin was ever ready to assist and to supply the necessary addition to my limited knowledge of the language in which it is my pleasure to publish this monograph in recollection of a most agreeable time spent in the United States.

P. Debye.

Leipzig, March 31, 1928.

CONTENTS

POLAR MOLECULES

CHAPTER I

FUNDAMENTAL ELECTROSTATIC FIELD RELATIONS

1. Electric Intensity, Electric Displacement and Electric Force.
The word polarity has been used in different ways to express molecular properties more or less connected with the actual arrangement, or the mobility, of the charges of which molecules are supposed to consist.[1] All definitions have, in common, the feature that they are based on the fundamental picture according to which a molecule may be represented as a system of electric charges, and at the outset it is not at all necessary to decide as to whether those charges have to be taken as discrete units, or if the natural phenomena can be better represented by introducing a continuous distribution, more in agreement with the picture in modern quantum theory. The fundamental proposition being the electrical viewpoint, it is obvious that we may expect to advance our knowledge of molecules by studying more closely their behavior under the influence of a disturbing electric field. This field may be an external field, subject to our control, or may be the field created by other neighboring molecular systems. In the last case we will ultimately obtain an electrical theory of the equation of state; in the first case we are dealing with dielectric and optical properties. As the last-named properties can be treated most simply, and still give us much insight into the molecular structure, we will in this treatise confine our attention chiefly to these dielectric and optical properties alone. A brief review of certain features of classical electrical theory will give the necessary foundation.

In the formal classical theory the influence of an insulator on an electric field is described correctly by the assumption that every element of volume dS acts as if it were the seat of an electric moment IdS. The factor I, the electric moment per unit volume, is called the polarization. Then if we consider a cylindrical cavity, of small cross section, with its axis in the direction of the lines of force, and bring into the interior of this cavity a unit charge, we call the actual force acting on this unit charge the electric intensity E. If, on the other hand, we make a cavity by employing the space between two

---

[1] See, *e.g.*, J. H. Hildebrand's book, "Solubility," p. 84, The Chemical Catalog Co., **1924.**

7

planes very near to each other and perpendicular to the lines of force, a unit charge situated between these planes will be acted upon by another force which we call the electric displacement D. This last named force D will be larger than E because of the induced charge on the two plane surfaces cut in the polarized insulator, the difference being $4\pi I$. Thus the equation

$$D = E + 4\pi I \qquad [1]$$

is a general relation and is independent of the form of the law connecting polarization and electric intensity.

The electric intensity E can be derived from a potential ϕ in the ordinary way as $-\text{grad } \phi$.

The total number of lines of displacement crossing a closed surface (counting them positive if they leave and negative if they enter the enclosed portion of space) is equal to 4π times the total charge contained in the interior of the surface.

These two well-known laws give the description of the fundamental properties of the electrostatic field and are sufficient provided the relation existing between displacement D and intensity E is known.

In Maxwell's formal theory the assumption is made that

$$D = \epsilon E, \qquad [2]$$

where ϵ is the dielectric constant. It is the molecular interpretation of ϵ which is to be the center of our interest in this book.

Let us assume that the actual electric intensity acting upon one molecule of the substance is called F, and that under the influence of this force the molecule takes up an electric moment, which when averaged over a certain length of time can be written

$$m = \alpha F. \qquad [3]$$

The molecular constant α we will call the "Polarizability," and our first step will be to determine how this molecular constant can be calculated if the dielectric constant ϵ is known. Two remarks have to be made in connection with relation [3]. In introducing a single constant α, that is, in stating that the average moment is in the direction of the force, we confine our attention to isotropic bodies, leaving out of consideration all directional crystalline properties. Moreover, in assuming proportionality between m and F, we merely introduce the fact that a dielectric *constant* exists, which is supported by experiment for a very large range in magnitudes of electric intensities. Only in considering dielectric saturation effects will it be necessary to depart from our assumption, expressed by [3].

2. Calculation of the Internal Field.

In introducing the polarizability we have made a differentiation between the actual intensity F, at the location of the molecule, and the classical intensities denoted by E and D. The next step, therefore, must be to find a connection between these three intensities. Suppose that we have a homogeneous field as would be created by a system of charges distributed uniformly over two conducting plates as shown by Figure 1, where the plates are supposed to be large as

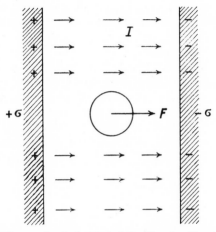

Fig. 1.   Diagram for derivation of the Clausius-Mosotti relation.

compared with their separation and the medium between the plates may be any dielectric. Let us calculate the actual force F acting upon a particle, carrying unit positive charge, which is located in the medium. This force may be thought of as consisting of three components

$$F = F_1 + F_2 + F_3.$$

By F_1 let us understand the force which is due to the charges distributed uniformly on the plates. This force is

$$F_1 = 4\pi\sigma, \qquad [4]$$

where σ is the surface density of charge on the plates. Now let us introduce a small sphere enclosing the particle in question. We will suppose that the radius of this sphere is large as compared with molecular dimensions but small as compared with ordinary macroscopic magnitudes. The component of force F_2 is then to be thought of as the additional force on the particle due to the presence of the dielectric, excluding the part contained within the small sphere. That is to say, F_2 is due to the polarization of the medium exterior to the small sphere, when the matter within it is supposed to be removed. The component F_2 is itself made up of two parts, first the force due to the layers of induced charge on the dielectric facing the conducting plates, and second the layer of charge on the surface of the small spherical cavity. It may be easily shown that the force F_2 is then

$$F_2 = -4\pi I + \frac{4\pi}{3} I, \qquad [5]$$

where I is the polarization of the medium, *i.e.*, the electric moment per unit volume set up in the dielectric. This equation is obtained using the well-known result that the magnitude of the normal component of the polarization vector is equal to the density of the induced charge on any boundary of the dielectric.

PROOF OF EQUATION [5].

First take the contribution to F_2 due to the induced charge facing the conducting plates. Since the surface density of the induced charge is equal to the magnitude of the polarization, this contribution is equal to $-4\pi I$, the negative sign indicating that directions to the right are counted as positive. Now we will calculate the contribution to F_2 due to the induced charge on the small spherical surface, letting ω denote a surface element, r the radius of the sphere, and θ the angle between r and I. The force on the interior particle is found by applying Coulomb's law to each element of charge by integration. The magnitude of the polarization I_n perpendicular to the spherical surface is $I \cos \theta$, and gives the density of the induced charge on this surface. We have only to consider contributions to the force which are in the same direction as I, so that we have the integral

$$\int_{\text{Surface}} \frac{I_n d\omega}{r^2} \cos \theta = 2 \int_0^{\pi/2} \frac{I \cos^2 \theta}{r^2} \cdot 2\pi r^2 \sin \theta d\theta = \frac{4\pi}{3} I.$$

It follows that the total contribution to F_2 is given by [5].

Finally, the component F_3 is the force due to the material contained within the small sphere. A general expression for F_3 cannot be given, but it may be evaluated in certain special cases. In the case of a cubical crystal, for example, it may be shown that the force F_3 is actually zero.[2] This result is also applicable to the case of liquids which are non-associated, *i.e.*, where the molecules are moving totally independently of each other. In general, however, F_3 is a very complicated function, and depends upon temperature, for instance. Let us now assume that $F_3 = 0$, and we have then for the total force

$$F = 4\pi\sigma - 4\pi I + \frac{4\pi}{3} I.$$

But according to the second fundamental law connecting the electric displacement D with the charges, we have

$$D = 4\pi\sigma.$$

[2] H. A. Lorentz, "Theory of Electrons," note 55, p. 303.

Finally, remembering equation [1], we find that [3]

$$F = E + \frac{4\pi}{3} I. \qquad [6]$$

This is the relation existing between the actual force F, the electric intensity E, and the polarization I, providing the assumption that $F_3 = 0$ can be made. It is on this relation that the classical law of Clausius and Mosotti, which will be treated in this text, is based. Our remark with respect to the ambiguity of the assumption $F_3 = 0$ shows that the application of this law may sometimes lead to erroneous conclusions about the molecular polarizability α, which we wish to determine by measuring the dielectric constant. The only possible way to avoid this difficulty seems to be not to consider for this purpose the ordinary measurements on liquids of comparatively high density, where the mutual interaction of the molecules is important, but to base the calculation on measurements of gases and perhaps diluted solutions, the molecules being mostly far enough apart so that their interaction may be neglected. In the case of gases, for instance, it will not be necessary to take into account either the second term $(4\pi/3)I$ in [6] or the force F_3, and the actual force F can then be identified with the electric intensity E.

3. The Relation of Clausius and Mosotti.

Assuming $F_3 = 0$, we found

$$F = E + 4\pi I.$$

If now the average moment of one molecule is

$$m = \alpha F,$$

as was assumed in [3], and if we let n be the number of molecules contained in 1 cc., then by the definition of the polarization I as the electric moment of 1 cc., we have

$$I = nm = n\alpha F = n\alpha \left(E + \frac{4\pi}{3} I \right). \qquad [7]$$

On the other hand the general relation [1] exists, giving

$$D = E + 4\pi I. \qquad [8]$$

It is only necessary to eliminate I between [7] and [8] in order to find the relation connecting D and E, i.e., to find the dielectric constant ϵ expressed in terms of the molecular polarizability α.

---

[3] While a homogeneous field was assumed, in deriving this equation for F, the final equation [6] is general, and is valid for any case in which $F_3 = 0$.

The result of this elimination can be put in the form

$$\frac{\epsilon - 1}{\epsilon + 2} = \frac{4\pi}{3} n\alpha. \qquad [9]$$

Expressed in words this relation states that, considering α as an invariable molecular constant, the quotient $(\epsilon - 1)/(\epsilon + 2)$ should be proportional to the density.[4] We prefer to write this equation in a somewhat different form by multiplying both sides with the quotient of the molecular weight M and the density ρ. For the left hand member we then get the expression

$$\frac{\epsilon - 1}{\epsilon + 2} \frac{M}{\rho}, \qquad [10]$$

while for the right hand member we get an expression involving the quotient nM/ρ, which is the number of molecules contained in one gram molecular weight, and is equal to Avogadro's Constant N ($N = 6.06 \times 10^{23}$). The right hand member of the equation thus obtained will be called the *Molar Polarization* and will be denoted by

$$P \equiv \frac{4\pi}{3} N\alpha = 2.54 \times 10^{24}\alpha. \qquad [11]$$

The molar polarization is a purely molecular quantity, giving some information about the electrical properties of the molecule. Combining [10] and [11] we find that it should be possible to calculate P by means of the equation

$$P = \frac{\epsilon - 1}{\epsilon + 2} \frac{M}{\rho}. \qquad [12]$$

It may be well to remark that P as well as α has the dimensions of volume. For actual substances the molar polarization ranges from a few cc. to some hundred cc. In the case of gases or vapors of small density the difference between ϵ and 1 will be very small. A good approximation may then be obtained if the denominator $\epsilon + 2$ in [12] is replaced by 3. In fact this approximation really means that we have considered $F = E$, and have neglected all interaction. In this case the calculation of the molar polarization can therefore be made with the help of the relation

$$P = \frac{\epsilon - 1}{3} \frac{M}{\rho}. \qquad [12']$$

If we assume moreover that the ideal gas laws hold, then the quotient M/ρ is the molar volume, which is equal to 22.4×10^3 cc. for

[4] O. F. Mosotti, *Mem. di Mathem. e di fisica in Modena*, **24**, II, 49, 1850; R. Clausius, "Die mechanische wärmetheorie," Vol. II, p. 62, Vieweg, **1879**.

zero degrees centigrade and one atmosphere pressure. Denoting by ϵ_0 the dielectric constant under these conditions we have the very simple relation

$$\alpha = 2.94 \times 10^{-21}(\epsilon_0 - 1).$$

Sometimes the attempt has been made to arrive at a better approximation for the interaction by introducing the assumption that the part F_3 of the actual force F, due to the interior of the sphere used in Section 1, does not equal zero, but like F_2 can be put proportional to the polarization I. If we assume

$$F_3 = q\frac{4\pi}{3}I$$

with a certain numerical factor q, which is supposed to be a measure of the interaction of the neighboring molecules, it is found that

$$\frac{\epsilon - 1}{(1 + q)\epsilon + (2 - q)} = \frac{4\pi}{3}n\alpha.$$

In this case the molar polarization P should therefore be calculated not by [12] but by the formula

$$P = \frac{\epsilon - 1}{(1 + q)\epsilon + (2 - q)}\frac{M}{\rho}.$$

This method of evaluating the interaction, however, can certainly not be expected to express the real interaction, and we will avoid making use of this more complicated expression, which would require the introduction of a new unknown constant q.[5]

Whereas the molar polarization is, according to our definition, the definite well-defined quantity $(4\pi/3)N\alpha$, it is obvious from the foregoing discussion that only for gases do we really know how to express this quantity in terms of the dielectric constant and density, as is done in [12']. In every other case, for instance, in the application of [12] to liquids, the calculation involves certain often questionable assumptions about the interaction with the surrounding molecules. The problem of the calculation of these interactions has, unfortunately, scarcely been treated in an adequate manner. It is indeed of the same difficulty as the problem involved in the calculation of the equation of state of real gases. It seems that valuable experimental as well as theoretical work could be done in studying the form of the equation expressing ϵ as a function of density and temperature, analogous to the ordinary equation of state which tells how the pressure depends upon the same variables. Such work can be expected to lead to a better understanding of the interaction of molecules.

Another interpretation can be given to equation [12] if we consider how P may depend upon the frequency. According to Maxwell's law that the formally introduced quantity ϵ has to be identified

[5] The literature is given very completely by K. Lichtenecker, *Physik. Z.*, **27**, 115 (1926).

with the square of the index of refraction r, the formula

$$\frac{r^2 - 1}{r^2 + 2} \frac{M}{\rho} = P = \frac{4\pi}{3} N\alpha \qquad [13]$$

results. The quantity P expressed in this way is called the *molar refraction*, and what we called the molar polarization can also be interpreted as the molar refraction for zero frequency. The relation [13] is known as the Lorentz-Lorenz relation,[6] and it has often been shown that in many cases it expresses, with a fair degree of approximation, the variation of the index of refraction over a large range of densities, if α is treated as an invariable constant. Although this is true for optical frequencies, it cannot be expected to hold equally well for zero frequency. In fact it will be shown that in general α cannot be considered as a constant for measurements at low frequencies.

[6] H. A. Lorentz, "Theory of Electrons"; *Ann. Physik.*, **9**, 641 (1880); Comm. Acad. Amsterdam, 1880; L. Lorenz, *Ann. Physik.*, **11**, 70 (1880); *Vidensk. Selsk. Skrifter*, **8**, 205 (1869); **10**, 485 (1875).

CHAPTER II

POLARIZABILITY AND MOLECULAR STRUCTURE

4. Earlier Interpretation of the Polarizability. Polarization by Distortion (Deformation).

Let us now assume that reliable values for α have been found experimentally. The immediate problem to be solved is what relation exists between α and other molecular properties. The oldest model for determining the behavior of a molecule in an electric field, already used by Clausius and by Mosotti, was that of a conductive sphere, say of radius a. Now from the classical equation for the electrostatic potential it is easily found that such a sphere, in a field of intensity F, will assume an electric moment

$$m = a^3 F.$$

In this picture the polarizability α is thus to be identified with the third power of the molecular radius, or, according to [11], the molar polarization P would be exactly equal to the real volume of the molecules contained in 1 mol, which we will denote by Ω. It is of interest to examine the extent to which this relation is valid. Let us therefore compare the value of $\Omega = P$ derived from measurements of ϵ with values of Ω derived from measurements of an entirely different nature. It is well known that in Van der Waals' equation

$$\left(p + \frac{a}{v^2} \right) (v - b) = RT,$$

expressing the pressure p as a function of the molar volume v and the absolute temperature T, the constant b represents 4 times the actual volume of the molecules contained 1 mol. We should thus compare $b/4$ with our former quantity Ω. As an example of such a comparison, for different kinds of molecules, Table I is given.

TABLE I. *Molecular Volume and Normal Polarization*

	$\Omega = b/4$	P
H_2	4.1	2.0
A	8.0	4.2
C_2H_4	14.0	9.4
C_5H_{12}	36.0	26.0

The values of b were calculated with the aid of the observed critical pressure p_k and critical temperature T_k. The latter are connected with the two constants a and b by the equations

$$p_k = \frac{1}{27}\frac{a}{b^2} \quad \text{and} \quad RT_k = \frac{8}{27}\frac{a}{b},$$

giving for b the formula actually used,

$$b = \frac{1}{8}\frac{RT_k}{p_k}.$$

It is indeed a very remarkable fact that, for the gases considered, the value of P found by the electrical method is in reality not very different from the value of Ω necessary to represent the deviations from the ideal gas laws. Table I suggests the rule that the molar polarization $[(\epsilon - 1)/(\epsilon + 2)]M/\rho$ may be roughly proportional to the quotient RT_k/p_k, although the factor is not exactly $1/32$. This is the form in which the rule has been enunciated by Ph. Guye [1] long ago.

Objections might be made to the calculation of b from Van der Waals' equation on the grounds that this equation does not represent the actual behavior of the gases, when a and b are taken as constants. A method of determining the "volume" of the molecules exists, however, which is independent of these assumptions. If at constant temperature the pressure p has been found as a function of the density, it will always be possible to express p in the form of a series arranged according to ascending negative powers of the molal volume v, so that

$$\frac{pv}{RT} = 1 + \frac{B_1}{v} + \frac{B_2}{v^2} + \cdots$$

The coefficients B_1, B_2, etc., are called virial coefficients. They depend on the temperature at which the measurements have been made and have therefore to be considered as temperature functions, which can be determined experimentally. If the potential energy E asociated with two molecules at any distance apart and for any mutual orientation is supposed to be known, a general and accurate formula can be derived to express B_1 as a function of the temperature. For the special case in which E is assumed to depend only upon the separation r, this formula is simply

$$B_1 = \frac{N}{2}\int (1 - e^{-(E/kT)})4\pi r^2 dr,$$

in which the integration has to be carried out over all values of r (N = Loschmidt's number, 6.06×10^{23}). If now the molecules are treated as hard spheres of diameter d, the first part of the integral corresponding to $o < r < d$ is $4\pi/3 \cdot d^3$, since for these values of r the potential energy has to be considered as being infinitely large, and the rest of the integral, corresponding to $d < r < \infty$, can be expanded in a series according to ascending powers of $1/T$. If therefore the experimental curve for the first virial coefficient B_1 is plotted, using $1/T$ as the variable, the limiting value of B_1 for $1/T = 0$ is $N/2 \cdot 4\pi/3 \cdot d^3$, and this is just four times the actual volume of the molecules, which is identical with the b used by Van der Waals. The coefficients of $1/T$, $1/T^2$, etc., give us information with respect to the volume integrals of E, E^2, etc. For He, H_2 and N_2 it has been found that for small values of $1/T$ there exists a deviation from the linear relation which this calculation predicts for the limiting form of the curve B_1 at high temperatures.

[1] Ph. A. Guye, *Compt. rend.*, **110**, 141 (1890); *Arch. Genève* (3) **23**, 197 and 204 (1890).

The actual values of B_1 are somewhat less than the ordinates of the straight line. This behavior is not mysterious however, and it could have been foreseen; the molecules will certainly not behave as absolutely rigid spheres, but will show a certain compressibility, as would be represented, for instance, by assuming repulsive forces proportional to a power function of the distance.[2] The deviations in question, therefore, merely express the dependence of the molecular diameter upon the kinetic energy with which the molecules collide. It would be justifiable, and indeed possible, to define the molecular diameter as the limiting value which would occur for molecules starting far apart with zero velocity.

The close connection exhibited in Table I between Ω and P, however, is not as general as this table suggests. It is due to the fact that a number of gases have been omitted—gases which when condensed form the so-called associated liquids.[3] To illustrate this point Table II is given, in which Ω has again been calculated from the critical pressure and the critical temperature, and P has been evaluated, taking for ϵ the value at ordinary room temperature.[4]

TABLE II. *Molecular Volume and Abnormal Polarization*

	Ω	P
NH_3	8.8	57
C_2H_5Cl	22	116
H_2S	7.9	30

For these gases the volume necessary to account for the dielectric properties in the sense of Mosotti's hypothesis is much larger than the volume derived from Van der Waals' equation. The essential point in Mosotti's hypothesis is the consideration of the molecule as a polarizable system, in which the moment in an electric field is set up by the force causing a displacement of the charges. A comparison between the two tables suggests that there may exist another reason why certain molecules can show polarization in an electric field. It is with the discussion of this second possibility that we are concerned in the next paragraphs. We have first to elucidate, however, that although Mosotti's conductive spheres are indeed antiquated, the modern assumptions about the constitution of atoms do not invalidate the main conclusions which have been drawn. For example let us consider Bohr's picture of the hydrogen atom; here we have a single electron describing an orbit, say of radius a. Let the plane of the orbit be perpendicular to the field F as shown in Figure 2. Due to the force

[2] Such an assumption has been treated by J. E. Jones, *Proc. Roy. Soc.* A. **106**, 463 (1924); A. **107**, 157 (1925); A. **112**, 214 (1926).
[3] Compare Turner, "Molecular Association."
[4] The ϵ-values for NH_3 and C_2H_5Cl were taken from the Landolt-Börnstein tables. H_2S has recently been measured by von Braunmühl, *Physik. Z.*, **28**, 141 (1927).

F the plane of the orbit will undergo a small shift ξ. To a first approximation the distance from the nucleus to the orbit will still be a, and the mean moment of the atom will be

$$m = e\xi.$$

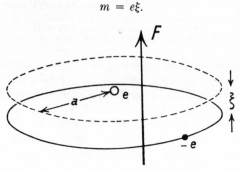

FIG. 2.   Distortion of the Bohr hydrogen atom in an electric field.

Now in order for the orbit indicated to be one of stable equilibrium we must have, on the assumption of the Coulomb law of force,

$$eF = \frac{e^2\xi}{a^2 \cdot a},$$

the factor ξ/a being introduced to give the vertical component of the Coulomb force. From this equation it is seen that

$$e\xi = m = a^3F.$$

The polarizability α is equal to a^3, and the only difference between this result and that based on Mosotti's hypothesis is that we have to introduce the radius of the orbit instead of the radius of his sphere. This will serve as an illustration, but it only holds for the special case in which the force is perpendicular to the orbit. In the most modern form of the quantum theory it has been necessary, in discussing the Stark effect, to calculate the potential energy of a hydrogen atom in an electric field. It was found that, for the unexcited state, this energy is equal to [5]

$$-\frac{9}{4}a^3F^2.$$

Now it can be shown that in general the potential energy of a polarizable system of polarizability α in a field of intensity F equals

$$-\frac{\alpha}{2}F^2.$$

[5] J. H. Van Vleck, *Proc. Nat. Acad.*, **12**, 662 (1926). .

The energy expression thus shows that

$$\alpha = \frac{9}{2}a^3,$$

stating again the proportionality of the polarizability with the third power of the radius of Bohr's orbit.

5. Additivity Rule. Effect of Temperature on the Polarization.

The discussion in the foregoing section points immediately to an ultimate subdivision of the molecules into two classes: class I containing molecules with normal values of the molar polarization, class II containing molecules with abnormally large values of this quantity. Further it is interesting to notice that in the attempt to apply the so-called additivity rule to the dielectric constant analogous conclusions can be drawn.

In optics it is well known that the index of refraction r of a more complicated molecule can be calculated, approximately, by assuming that the molar refraction of a compound

$$\frac{r^2 - 1}{r^2 + 2} \frac{M}{\rho}$$

is a sum of atomic refractions, each one of which is a characteristic constant identified with a corresponding constituent atom. Even in chemical combination, therefore, an atom retains approximately its characteristic polarizability. Now it can be asked if the same rule would apply for the dielectric constant, substituting for the molar refraction the molar polarization

$$P = \frac{\epsilon - 1}{\epsilon + 2} \frac{M}{\rho}.$$

This has often been tried, with the result that the rule is found to apply in some cases, but in other cases, especially for substances with high dielectric constants, it is certainly wrong.[6] The deviations seem to be due partly to the existence of special groups like OH or NH_2 in the molecular formula; but this is not the only cause, the special arrangement of such groups in the chemical formula is also of great importance. Without going into further detail, we can deduce that considerations on the applicability of the additivity rule also point to a subdivision of molecules into two different classes, our former class I being the one for which the additivity rule holds.

The more or less definite suggestions contained in the preceding discussion attain a definite form when we consider thirdly the effect

[6] Ch. B. Thwing, *Z. phys. Chem.*, **14**, 286 (1894); P. Walden, *ibid.*, **10**, 569 (1910).

of temperature on the dielectric constant. Suppose we are dealing with gases or vapours and we measure the dielectric constant at different temperatures but keeping the density constant, such that every unit of volume always contains the same number of molecules. Of course it is also possible to keep the pressure constant, as has often been done in the experiments, but then we have to reduce the measurements to constant densities. In fact this is done if we calculate the molar polarization by the formula

$$P = \frac{\epsilon - 1}{3} \frac{M}{\rho},$$

taking account of the change in the density ρ.

Experiments of this kind, showing the peculiar effect we are going to discuss, were first carried out by Baedeker.[7] He found that for some gases the molar polarization is really constant, but that other gases give decreasing values of P with increasing temperature. This leads directly to the classification ultimately adopted. In class I we will place the molecules of the first kind, while class II will contain the molecules for which P depends on temperature. As an example of the second class we take NH_3 as measured by Jona,[8] illustrating its behaviour by the values of Table III.

TABLE III. *Temperature Effect of Polarization for Ammonia*

T	P (cc.)
292.2	57.57
309.0	55.01
333.0	51.22
387.0	44.99
413.0	42.51
446.0	39.59

As a first step towards the explanation let us consider a very simple model of a system, in which the polarization is due to a distortion effect, and investigate the possibility of such a model giving us a polarizability depending on temperature. A charge e may be connected to a center by a force which is proportional to its displacement ξ from this center. Putting for this force $f\xi$ and for the intensity of the field F, the equilibrium condition gives

$$f\xi = eF,$$

and for the induced moment

$$m = e\xi = \frac{e^2}{f}F.$$

[7] K. Baedeker, *Z. phys. Chem.*, **36**, 315 (1901).
[8] M. Jona, *Phys. Z.*, **20**, 14 (1919).

Now suppose that our system is in temperature equilibrium with its surroundings; then the charge will make irregular oscillations, and the question is if these oscillations will change the induced moment. It can be seen at once that this is not the case, for since the restoring force is proportional to the displacement a diminution of the moment by a certain amount will involve the same change in potential energy as an increase by the same amount. Therefore both corresponding positions of the charge will be equally probable and in the average the electric moment will have the same value as given before, independent of the intensity of its heat motion.

The same result is of course found by applying the appropriate method of calculation. The charge displaced over a distance ξ has taken up the potential energy

$$\int f\xi d\xi = \frac{f}{2}\xi^2$$

due to the restoring force, and its potential energy in the electric field is

$$- e\xi F.$$

The total potential energy is thus

$$u = \frac{f}{2}\xi^2 - eF\xi.$$

Now according to the Boltzmann-Maxwell principle the probability that in our system the charge will be found at a place between ξ and $\xi + d\xi$ is proportional to

$$e^{-(u/kT)}d\xi,$$

where $k = 1.37 \times 10^{-16}$ ergs = Boltzmann's constant. Remembering that $e\xi$ is the electric moment, we deduce that the mean moment $\overline{m}$ will be

$$\overline{m} = \frac{\int e\xi e^{-(u/kT)}d\xi}{\int e^{-(u/kT)}d\xi}.$$

Introducing a new variable

$$\eta = \xi - \frac{eF}{f},$$

the energy u takes the form

$$u = -\frac{e^2F^2}{2f} + \frac{f}{2}\eta^2$$

and we find for $\overline{m}$ the expression

$$\overline{m} = \frac{\int\left[\frac{e^2F}{f} + e\eta\right]e^{-(f/2kT)\eta^2}\,d\eta}{\int e^{-(f/2kT)\eta^2}d\eta}.$$

The integration is to be carried out from $\eta = -\infty$ to $\eta = +\infty$. The integral corresponding to the second term in the numerator is zero; therefore

$$\overline{m} = \frac{e^2F}{f},$$

that is, the equilibrium value.

As will be seen in the following pages this result is quite general, in the sense that it holds for a general system of charges, providing only that the restoring forces are linear functions of the displacements. But this is the condition necessary for the existence of a dielectric constant independent of the intensity of the field. Thus even if the system is in classical temperature equilibrium with its surroundings, its mean electric moment will not depend upon temperature. As long as we do not depart from the ordinary picture, which attributes the polarization to a distortion effect, it is impossible to understand why molecules exist which show the temperature effect.

Now in the theory of paramagnetism we are accustomed to assume that the paramagnetic effect is due to the pre-existence of molecules which carry a permanent magnetic moment and can be oriented by the field like small magnets. Nothing prevents us from making the assumption that, in general, although the molecule is uncharged, the center of the positive charges may not be at the same point as the center of the negative charges. If this occurs, then the molecule has a permanent electric moment and now can show a polarization not only by distortion, but also by orientation; for the orientation of smallest potential energy will be such that the electric moment points in the direction of the external field. We may expect that the amount of orientation created by the field will be larger the smaller the disturbance due to temperature motion. In fact this is the explanation offered for molecules of class II. By establishing the quantitative law for the dependence of orientation upon temperature we will be enabled to derive from measurements of the temperature variation of the dielectric constant the absolute value of the electric moment. Calling molecules of class II *polar molecules*, we will therefore arrive at a definite measure of their polarity, in absolute electrostatic units. Some general considerations relating to the characteristics of an electrical system will have first to be considered.

6. General Considerations on the Electrical Constants Characterizing a Molecule.

In order to arrive at a general classification of the different types of molecules we will analyze the potential energy of an arbitrary distribution of charges in an external field. If the charges are not to be considered as at rest we will fix our attention on a time average, distributing the charge over every element of the orbits proportionate to the time it takes to cover the respective elements.[1] Now let us consider a given molecule containing any number of charges e_i with coordinates (ξ_i, η_i, ζ_i) relative to a system of rectangular axes x, y, z, where the origin O may be taken within the molecule but is otherwise arbitrary. Letting φ denote the potential of the

---

[1] In modern quantum theory it is still more natural to consider such an average distribution of charge.

external field at the origin, the potential at $(\xi_i,\ \eta_i,\ \zeta_i)$ may be written

$$\varphi_i = \varphi + \left(\xi_i \frac{\partial \varphi}{\partial x} + \eta_i \frac{\partial \varphi}{\partial y} + \zeta_i \frac{\partial \varphi}{\partial z} \right) + \frac{1}{2} \left(\xi_i^2 \frac{\partial^2 \varphi}{\partial x^2} + \eta_i^2 \frac{\partial^2 \varphi}{\partial y^2} \right.$$
$$\left. + \zeta_i^2 \frac{\partial^2 \varphi}{\partial z^2} + 2\xi_i \eta_i \frac{\partial^2 \varphi}{\partial x \partial y} + 2\eta_i \zeta_i \frac{\partial^2 \varphi}{\partial y \partial z} + 2\zeta_i \xi_i \frac{\partial^2 \varphi}{\partial z \partial x} \right) + \cdots.$$

The potential energy of the molecule is

$$\sum e_i \varphi_i = \sum e_i \varphi + \sum \left(e_i \xi_i \frac{\partial \varphi}{\partial x} + e_i \eta_i \frac{\partial \varphi}{\partial y} + e_i \zeta_i \frac{\partial \varphi}{\partial z} \right)$$
$$+ \frac{1}{2} \sum \left(e_i \xi_i^2 \frac{\partial^2 \varphi}{\partial x^2} + \cdots + 2\xi_i \eta_i e_i \frac{\partial^2 \varphi}{\partial x \partial y} + \cdots \right) + \cdots. \quad [14]$$

In this expression φ, $\partial \varphi/\partial x$, $\partial^2 \varphi/\partial x^2$, etc., have to be considered as constants defining the field, the molecule itself being characterized by certain sums ranging over the products of the charges with their coordinates. The first of these sums $\sum e_i$ is the total charge. Thus for an uncharged molecule the first term in [14] does not exist. In the second term the energy is expressed with the help of three molecular constants

$$\sum e_i \xi_i, \quad \sum e_i \eta_i, \quad \sum e_i \zeta_i.$$

We can consider these three sums as the three components of the electric moment [2] $\mathbf{m}$. On the other hand

$$- \frac{\partial \varphi}{\partial x}, \quad - \frac{\partial \varphi}{\partial y}, \quad - \frac{\partial \varphi}{\partial z}$$

are the three rectangular components of the field intensity $\mathbf{E}$. The second term therefore has the form

$$- (\mathbf{m}\mathbf{E}),$$

denoting the scalar product by round brackets. A molecule for which the electric moment has a finite value is called a *polar molecule* and its polarity is measured by the absolute value of $\mathbf{m}$.

It may be that the dissymmetry necessary for a finite value of m does not exist. Then the second energy term is zero also. In this case it is seen from [14] that we have to characterize the molecule by six constants

$$\theta_{11} = \sum e_i \xi_i^2, \qquad \theta_{12} = \sum e_i \xi_i \eta_i,$$
$$\theta_{22} = \sum e_i \eta_i^2, \qquad \theta_{23} = \sum e_i \eta_i \zeta_i,$$
$$\theta_{33} = \sum e_i \zeta_i^2, \qquad \theta_{31} = \sum e_i \zeta_i \xi_i,$$

[2] Where necessary, vectors will always be indicated by bold-faced type.

and the energy will depend on the space variation of the external field. The six constants θ are known as the quadrupole moments or the electric moments of inertia. The potential energy due to the electric moment exists in a homogeneous field; this is why measurements of the dielectric constant will lead to a determination of m. The energy due to the moments of inertia, however, exists only in a non-homogeneous field. As the non-homogeneity of an external field can naturally be made only very small within the distances covered by a molecular system, no experimental evidence of this energy term has yet been observed in external fields. Only the interaction of molecules as derived from deviations of the ideal gas laws gives us some experimental information of the magnitudes of the moments of the second order. The six constants θ really can be reduced to only three, for by a proper orientation of the system of coordinates θ_{12}, θ_{23} and θ_{31} may be made to vanish.

Now a system is imaginable of such a high order of inner symmetry that $\theta_{11} = \theta_{22} = \theta_{33}$. In this case the third energy term in [14] would also be zero, as φ has to be a solution of Laplace's equation. It would then be necessary to characterize the molecules by the still larger number of constants entering in the next term, but no experiments are known dealing with these constants.

The same classification of rigid electrical systems may be derived in another way, considering not the potential energy in an external field, but the distribution of the potential due to the system itself.

Suppose we know any potential $\varphi(x, y, z)$ to be characterized by the fact that it is a solution of Laplace's equation. If then instead of x, y, z we substitute $x - \xi$, $y - \eta$, and $z - \zeta$, taking ξ, η, ζ as constants, the new potential φ' will again be a solution of the fundamental equation. The same is true of the difference $\varphi - \varphi'$. Now we can multiply this difference by an arbitrary constant and pass to the limit $\xi = 0$, $\eta = 0$, $\zeta = 0$. If then we assume the product of the arbitrary constant with any of the values ξ, η, ζ to pass to a finite value we have found a new solution, in fact by differentiating the first one. This process we can repeat and so get an infinite number of different solutions. Starting with the fundamental potential e/r corresponding to a point charge e, and adding the potentials we get consecutively, the result is

$$
\begin{aligned}
\varphi = \frac{e}{r} &- \left[\mu_1 \frac{\partial}{\partial x}\left(\frac{1}{r}\right) + \mu_2 \frac{\partial}{\partial y}\left(\frac{1}{r}\right) + \mu_3 \frac{\partial}{\partial z}\left(\frac{1}{r}\right) \right] \\
&+ \frac{1}{2}\left[\theta_{11}\frac{\partial^2}{\partial x^2}\left(\frac{1}{r}\right) + \theta_{22}\frac{\partial^2}{\partial y^2}\left(\frac{1}{r}\right) + \theta_{33}\frac{\partial^2}{\partial z^2}\left(\frac{1}{r}\right) \right. \\
&+ \left. 2\theta_{12}\frac{\partial^2}{\partial x \partial y}\left(\frac{1}{r}\right) + 2\theta_{23}\frac{\partial^2}{\partial y \partial z}\left(\frac{1}{r}\right) + 2\theta_{31}\frac{\partial^2}{\partial z \partial x}\left(\frac{1}{r}\right) \right] + \cdots .
\end{aligned} \tag{15}
$$

The constants μ_1, μ_2, μ_3 represent the limiting values of $e\xi$, $e\eta$, $e\zeta$, etc. Every following term in the series is of the next higher order in $1/r$, the first being of the order $1/r$, the second of the order $1/r^2$, etc. Calling the power factor in general r^{-n-1} and taking this factor outside in the expression for the corresponding potential, the remaining functions depend only on x/r, y/r, z/r; they represent the surface harmonics of order n, as they have been introduced by J. C. Maxwell.[3]

It has to be borne in mind that the different functions introduced by the differentiations in [15] are not all independent, owing to the fact that $1/r$ is itself a solution of Laplace's equation. Therefore

$$\frac{\partial^2}{\partial x^2}\left(\frac{1}{r}\right) + \frac{\partial^2}{\partial y^2}\left(\frac{1}{r}\right) + \frac{\partial^2}{\partial z^2}\left(\frac{1}{r}\right) = 0$$

and the third term in [15], for instance, contains only five independent functions instead of six, as it would appear at first sight. In general the surface harmonic of order n contains $2n + 1$ arbitrary constants.

The physical interpretation of the different functions in [15] is illustrated by Figures 3, 4, and 5. Figure 3 represents a positive

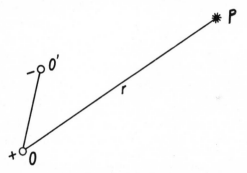

FIG. 3.   Dipole.

and a negative charge separated by a finite distance, the second term of [15] being the limiting form of the corresponding potential when the separation is infinitely small. We refer to this combination of two charges by calling it a *dipole*. If we transfer this dipole parallel to itself in an arbitrary direction, change the sign of the charges, and consider the configuration consisting of the original dipole and the transferred dipole, we get the *quadrupole* of Figure 4. Passing to the limit again, its potential is represented by the third term in [15]. The next configuration, constructed by a displacement of the quadrupole in an arbitrary direction, will give the

[3] J. C. Maxwell, "Treatise on Electricity and Magnetism," Vol. I, p. 130, 160; Courant-Hilbert, "Mathematische Physik," Vol. I, p. 420.

octupole of Figure 5, with a corresponding potential function to be represented by a fourth term in [15], etc. In order to arrive at the

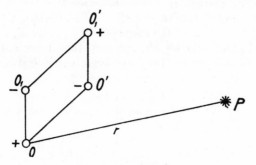

FIG. 4. Quadrupole.

physical interpretation of the constants measuring the magnitude of the moments of different order, which have been introduced, we consider first a charge e_i with the coordinates ξ_i, η_i, ζ_i and a point P

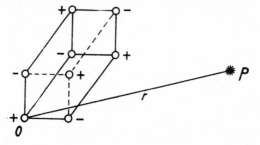

FIG. 5. Octupole.

with the coordinates x, y, z, at a large distance from the charge. The potential φ_i at P due to the charge is

$$\varphi_i = \frac{e_i}{\sqrt{(x - \xi_i)^2 + (y - \eta_i)^2 + (z - \zeta_i)^2}}.$$

If now we develop this expression according to positive powers of ξ_i, η_i, ζ_i, we find

$$\varphi_i = \frac{e_i}{r} - \left[e_i\xi_i\frac{\partial}{\partial x}\left(\frac{1}{r}\right) + e_i\eta_i\frac{\partial}{\partial y}\left(\frac{1}{r}\right) + e_i\zeta_i\frac{\partial}{\partial z}\left(\frac{1}{r}\right) \right]$$
$$+ \frac{1}{2}\left[e_i\xi_i^2\frac{\partial^2}{\partial x^2}\left(\frac{1}{r}\right) + e_i\eta_i^2\frac{\partial^2}{\partial y^2}\left(\frac{1}{r}\right) + e_i\zeta_i^2\frac{\partial^2}{\partial z^2}\left(\frac{1}{r}\right) \right.$$
$$\left. + 2e_i\xi_i\eta_i\frac{\partial^2}{\partial x\partial y}\left(\frac{1}{r}\right) + 2e_i\eta_i\zeta_i\frac{\partial^2}{\partial y\partial z}\left(\frac{1}{r}\right) + 2e_i\zeta_i\xi_i\frac{\partial^2}{\partial z\partial x}\left(\frac{1}{r}\right) \right]$$
$$+ \cdots,$$

where $r = \sqrt{x^2 + y^2 + z^2}$ represents the distance from P to the origin of the system of coordinates. Let us now consider a system of charges e_i. Its potential will be given by

$$\varphi = \sum \varphi_i,$$

and this expression will have the same form as [15]. Remembering that each following term in [15] is of the next higher order in $1/r$, we can interpret the formula in the following manner.

At a large distance the potential of any distribution of charges is given to a first approximation by the first term of [15], provided we put

$$e = \sum e_i.$$

A better approximation is obtained by adding the second term; that is, by introducing the potential of a dipole, provided the three components of its moment are taken to be

$$\mu_1 = \sum e_i \xi_i, \qquad \mu_2 = \sum e_i \eta_i, \qquad \mu_3 = \sum e_i \zeta_i.$$

A still better approximation is obtained by introducing the third term, corresponding to a quadrupole, etc. The very first term only appears in the case of ions, while the first possible electrical characteristic of an uncharged molecule is its electric moment, that is, the moment of the corresponding dipole with the three components μ_1, μ_2, μ_3. For more symmetrical molecules this moment will equal zero, and then we would have to introduce the quadrupole with its constants, etc. It is thus seen that from our second point of view we arrive at the same classification as before, and obtain the same formulas for the electrical constants which will characterize the molecule.

7. Polarization by Orientation.   Effect of Temperature.

Suppose we can consider the molecule as a rigid system of charges, denoting by **m** its electric moment and by **F** the intensity of the field. According to [14] the potential energy u of the molecule will be expressed by the equation·

$$u = - (\mathbf{mF}).$$

If no forces at all are acting, the moments of a number of molecules will, on the average, be distributed with the same probability over all directions in space. Thus the number of molecules pointing in the directions confined within a solid angle $d\Omega$, shown by Figure 6, is

$$A \, d\Omega,$$

where A is a constant depending on the number of molecules considered. In a field of intensity F, however, the number confined to

$d\Omega$ will be, according to Boltzmann's law,

$$A\, e^{-(u/KT)} d\Omega.$$

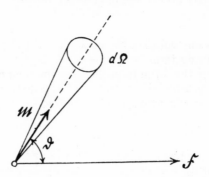

Fig. 6. Diagram for space orientation of dipoles.

Now introducing ϑ, the angle between the directions of m and F, gives

$$u = -\,\mu F \cos \vartheta,$$

where μ is the absolute value of the electric moment.   A specific molecule pointing in the direction of $d\Omega$ has a component $\mu \cos \vartheta$ in the direction of the field.   We therefore find the average moment $\overline{m}$ in the direction of the field, of one molecule, in calculating the expression

$$\overline{m} = \frac{\displaystyle\int A\, e^{(\mu F/KT)\cos\vartheta} \mu \cos \vartheta\, d\Omega}{\displaystyle\int A\, e^{(\mu F/KT)\cos\vartheta}\, d\Omega},$$

where the integration is taken over all possible directions.   Introducing

$$\frac{\mu F}{KT} = x, \qquad\qquad [16]$$

the result can be expressed by the equation [4]

$$\frac{\overline{m}}{\mu} = \operatorname{cotgh} x - \frac{1}{x} = L(x). \qquad\qquad [17]$$

The result can most easily be found in the following way.   Remembering that

$$d\Omega = 2\pi \sin \vartheta d\vartheta;$$

[4] Cotgh x means the hyperbolic cotangent of x, defined by

$$\operatorname{cotgh} x = \frac{e^x + e^{-x}}{e^x - e^{-x}}.$$

and introducing $\xi = \cos \vartheta$ as a new variable, it is found that

$$\frac{\overline{m}}{\mu} = \frac{\int_{-1}^{+1} e^{x\xi}\xi d\xi}{\int_{-1}^{+1} e^{x\xi}d\xi} \, .$$

We then observe that the numerator of this expression is the differential coefficient of the denominator with respect to x. But for the denominator it is found at once that

$$\int_{-1}^{+1} e^{x\xi}d\xi = \frac{e^x - e^{-x}}{2} \, .$$

Differentiating this expression with respect to x to find the numerator, and then calculating the quotient of numerator and denominator will give formula [17].

Figure 7 represents the right-hand side of equation [17] as a function of $x = \mu F/KT$. It shows how a saturation effect occurs at very large intensities.

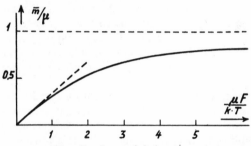

FIG. 7.   Langevin's function.

The calculation of the mean electric moment resembles the calculation first made by P. Langevin [5] to find the mean magnetic moment of gas molecules carrying a permanent magnetic moment. That is why we call the characteristic function of x appearing in [17] Langevin's function $L(x)$. Even in our case, where we are dealing with electric moments, the experimental conditions are very often such that $x = \mu F/KT$ is a very small number. In this case we can replace $L(x)$ by its first approximation

$$L(x) = \frac{x}{3},$$

with the result that

$$\overline{m} = \frac{\mu^2}{3KT} F. \qquad [18]$$

For sufficiently small field intensities the apparent average moment of one molecule is thus proportional to the field intensity, although now it has not been created by a distortion of the molecular system.

[5] P. Langevin, *J. phys.*, (4) **4**, 678 (1905); *Ann. chim. phys.*, (8) **5**, 70 (1905).

But as we were led to expect at the end of Section 5, the polarizability·
is not a constant but depends on temperature, decreasing with increasing temperature.

The foregoing calculation has been carried out for a rigid system,
in which the external field is supposed to induce no change at all.
But from our classification of molecules into two groups we know
that in making this supposition we are going too far. Combining
the result found in Section 5 for the simple model of an elastic
molecule with our present result, we have to expect that, in general,
the mean electric moment $\overline{m}$ will be expressed by [6]

$$\overline{m} = \left(\alpha_0 + \frac{\mu^2}{3KT} \right) F. \qquad [19]$$

The factor α_0 takes care of the distortion effect, the factor $\mu^2/3KT$
of the orientation effect. However, from a mathematical point of
view, we ought to be dissatisfied with this derivation of the fundamental equation [19]. That is why in the next section (Section 8)
we take up the question again. By this more general treatment
the same formula will be found, but we will have the advantage of
finding a more satisfactory interpretation of the constant α_0.

8. More General Derivation of the Formula for the Polarizability.

It remains to be shown that [19] is a very general equation for
the polarizability and to establish the connection between the
constant α_0 and optical phenomena. For this purpose let us again
consider the molecule as a configuration built up of a number of
charges e_i, but we now suppose that we have to do with an elastic
system which will be distorted in an external field. The rest-
coordinates [7] of any charge e_i will be called ξ_i, η_i, ζ_i and the components of the displacement u_i, v_i, w_i. If the whole system has no
total charge, then according to [14] the energy u' due to the existence
of an external field, with the components X, Y, Z, will be

$$u' = - \sum e_i[(\xi_i + u_i)X + (\eta_i + v_i)Y + (\zeta_i + w_i)Z].$$

The distortion characterized by the displacement with the components u_i, v_i, w_i will correspond to an internal energy u'', and we
will assume that this internal energy is a homogeneous quadratic
function Q of all the variables u_i, v_i, w_i. In this way we make the

---

[6] For the interpretation of the temperature effect the electric moment was
first introduced by P. Debye, *Physik. Z.*, **13**, 97 (1912), where formula [19] is
given. Sir J. J. Thomson published a note on the same subject and with the same
result in the *Phil. Mag.*, **28**, 757 (1914). He treats the subject again in his lectures
delivered at the Franklin Institute on "The Electron in Chemistry," 1923, p. 42,
without reference to the literature.

[7] By the rest-coordinates of a charge are meant the coordinates the charge
would have if the molecule were not distorted. The term displacement refers to
a change in the rest-coordinates.

most general supposition consistent with the existence of a dielectric constant, because this is the only way to provide for a distortion which gives a moment linear in X, Y, Z. The total energy

$$u = u' + u'' = u' + Q$$

has its minimum value for the equilibrium case. We therefore would be able to calculate the values of u_i, v_i, w_i by solving the linear equations we derive on equating the differential coefficients of u, with respect to any u_i, v_i, or w_i, to zero. These equations have the form

$$\left. \begin{aligned} \frac{\partial Q}{\partial u_i} &= e_i X, \\[2mm] \frac{\partial Q}{\partial v_i} &= e_i Y, \\[2mm] \frac{\partial Q}{\partial w_i} &= e_i Z. \end{aligned} \right\} \qquad [20]$$

To find the total energy u of the system in the equilibrium state, we have to introduce in u' and Q the values of u_i, v_i, w_i, which are supposed to be calculated in solving the equations [20]. For our purpose, however, the actual calculation is not necessary, for since Q is a homogeneous quadratic function Euler's theorem is applicable, stating that

$$2Q = \sum \left(u_i \frac{\partial Q}{\partial u_i} + v_i \frac{\partial Q}{\partial v_i} + w_i \frac{\partial Q}{\partial w_i} \right).$$

Remembering the equations [20], it is therefore possible to express the equilibrium value of the total energy

$$u = u' + Q$$

in the form

$$\left. \begin{aligned} u = &- (X \sum e_i \xi_i + Y \sum e_i \eta_i + Z \sum e_i \zeta_i) \\ &- \tfrac{1}{2} (X \sum e_i u_i + Y \sum e_i v_i + Z \sum e_i w_i). \end{aligned} \right\} \quad [21]$$

This formal representation of the equilibrium value of the energy shows that this quantity consists of two parts, the first being the negative scalar product of the field intensity and the permanent moment, and the second one half of the negative scalar product of the field intensity and the induced moment. Now according to [20] the displacements u_i, v_i, w_i are linear functions of X, Y, Z, and it follows from the second term of [21] that Q, which is represented by this term, can be expressed as a homogeneous quadratic function of the field components X, Y, Z. If it is expressed in this way we will denote it by Q^*, such that

$$Q^* = \tfrac{1}{2}[a_{11}X^2 + a_{22}Y^2 + a_{33}Z^2$$
$$+ 2a_{12}XY + 2a_{23}YZ + 2a_{31}ZX]. \qquad [22]$$

The constants $a_{11} \cdots a_{31}$ could be expressed as functions of the coefficients entering in the equations [20], but it is not necessary to carry out this calculation. For we can suppose our molecule as characterized well enough for our purpose by the six constants $a_{11} \cdots a_{31}$. To have a picture we can, in the usual way, consider the surface on which we have to move the end of the field intensity vector with the components X, Y, Z in order to keep Q^*, and therefore the distortion energy, constant. According to [22] this will be an ellipsoid, in general with three different axes, oriented in a definite way in the molecule. Introducing the three constants

$$\mu_1 = \sum e_i \xi_i, \qquad \mu_2 = \sum e_i \eta_i, \qquad \mu_3 = \sum e_i \zeta_i,$$

which are the three components of the permanent moment, we now have for the equilibrium energy, according to [21], the explicit form

$$u = - (\mu_1 X + \mu_2 Y + \mu_3 Z)$$
$$- \tfrac{1}{2}(a_{11}X^2 + a_{22}Y^2 + a_{33}Z^2 + 2a_{12}XY + 2a_{23}YZ \qquad [23]$$
$$+ 2a_{31}ZX).$$

If we remark that the second term in [23] is again a homogeneous quadratic function, this time of X, Y, Z, it becomes evident on applying Euler's theorem and comparing [21] with [23] that the components m_x, m_y, m_z of the total electric moment of our system can be expressed by the well-known formulas

$$m_x = - \frac{\partial u}{\partial X}, \qquad m_y = - \frac{\partial u}{\partial Y}, \qquad m_z = - \frac{\partial u}{\partial Z}. \qquad [24]$$

In fact this comparison shows that

$$\sum e_i u_i = - \frac{\partial Q^*}{\partial X}, \qquad \sum e_i v_i = - \frac{\partial Q^*}{\partial Y}, \qquad \sum e_i w_i = - \frac{\partial Q^*}{\partial Z}.$$

These three quantities are the three components of the induced moment, which we have to add to the corresponding three components of the permanent moment to get the components of the total moment.

We start now with equation [23] for the equilibrium energy of our system and apply Boltzmann's theorem to find the mean electric moment of this system in an electric field of intensity **F**. For this purpose let the coordinate axes be rigidly imbedded in a given molecule. Let the z-axis be enclosed in a solid angle $d\Omega$ and let ψ denote the angle of rotation about the z-axis. Since all orientations of the molecule are equally probable if no external field exists, it follows that in the presence of such a field the number of molecules of which the orientation is characterized by $d\Omega$ and $d\psi$ is

$$A e^{-(u/KT)} d\Omega d\psi.$$

Letting m_f denote the component of the moment in the direction of **F**, it follows that the mean moment $\overline{m}_f$ of the molecule, in the direction of **F**, is given by the equation

$$\overline{m}_f = \frac{\displaystyle\int e^{-(u/KT)} m_f d\Omega d\psi}{\displaystyle\int e^{-(u/KT)} d\Omega d\psi}. \qquad [25]$$

Taking account of the general relation [24], the moment of a given molecule in the direction of **F** is

$$m_f = -\left(\alpha \frac{\partial u}{\partial X} + \beta \frac{\partial u}{\partial Y} + \gamma \frac{\partial u}{\partial Z} \right),$$

where α, β, γ are the direction cosines of **F**. Now let **s** denote a unit vector in the direction of **F**, which we will write in the form

$$\mathbf{s} = i\alpha + j\beta + k\gamma,$$

introducing the three unit vectors i, j, k in the three directions of x, y, z, respectively. Furthermore let **D**u be a vector with components $\partial u/\partial X$, $\partial u/\partial Y$, $\partial u/\partial Z$, such that

$$\mathbf{D}u = i \frac{\partial u}{\partial X} + j \frac{\partial u}{\partial Y} + k \frac{\partial u}{\partial Z}.$$

It follows from these definitions that

$$m_f = -(\mathbf{s}\mathbf{D}u),$$

and the mean moment in the direction of **F** may then be written as

$$\overline{m}_f = \frac{\displaystyle\int e^{[1/KT](f_1+f_2)} [(\mathbf{s}\mathbf{D}f_1) + (\mathbf{s}\mathbf{D}f_2)] d\Omega d\psi}{\displaystyle\int e^{[1/KT](f_1+f_2)} d\Omega d\psi}, \qquad [25']$$

introducing

$$f_1 = \mu_1 X + \mu_2 Y + \mu_3 Z,$$

and

$$f_2 = \tfrac{1}{2}[a_{11}X^2 + a_{22}Y^2 + a_{33}Z^2 + 2a_{12}XY + 2a_{23}YZ + 2a_{31}ZX].$$

2

In order to integrate this expression both the numerator and denominator may be expanded in series, giving

$$\overline{m}_f = \frac{\overline{(\mathbf{sD}f_1)} + \overline{(\mathbf{sD}f_2)} + \dfrac{1}{KT}\overline{f_1(\mathbf{sD}f_1)} + \cdots}{1 + \dfrac{1}{KT}\overline{f_1} + \cdots},$$

where the bars are used to denote averages. For example

$$\overline{(\mathbf{sD}f_1)} = \frac{\displaystyle\int (\mathbf{sD}f_1)d\Omega d\psi}{\displaystyle\int d\Omega d\psi}.$$

The dots in the above equation for $\overline{m}_f$ indicate terms of the second and higher order in F, but since we are not concerned with saturation effects, only the first order terms have to be considered. Now observe first that

$$\overline{(\mathbf{sD}f_1)} = \overline{(\alpha\mu_1 + \beta\mu_2 + \gamma\mu_3)} = \overline{\mu \cos (\mathbf{s}, \mu)}.$$

The average value of the cosine is zero and it follows that

$$\overline{(\mathbf{sD}f_1)} = 0.$$

The second term to be calculated is

$$\begin{aligned}
(\mathbf{sD}f_2) &= \alpha(a_{11}X + a_{12}Y + a_{13}Z) \\
&\quad + \beta(a_{21}X + a_{22}Y + a_{23}Z) \\
&\quad + \gamma(a_{31}Z + a_{32}Y + a_{33}Z) \\
&= \alpha(a_{11}\alpha + a_{12}\beta + a_{13}\gamma)F \\
&\quad + \beta(a_{21}\alpha + a_{22}\beta + a_{23}\gamma)F \\
&\quad + \gamma(a_{31}\alpha + a_{32}\beta + a_{33}\gamma)F.
\end{aligned}$$

But it is evident that

$$\overline{\alpha\beta} = \overline{\beta\gamma} = \overline{\gamma\alpha} = 0,$$

whereas [8]

$$\overline{\alpha^2} = \overline{\beta^2} = \overline{\gamma^2} = \tfrac{1}{3}.$$

Hence we have

$$\overline{(\mathbf{sD}f_2)} = \frac{a_{11} + a_{22} + a_{33}}{3} F.$$

[8] The relation $\alpha^2 + \beta^2 + \gamma^2 = 1$ holds; moreover $\overline{\alpha^2} = \overline{\beta^2} = \overline{\gamma^2}$, giving the result of the text.

The third term of the numerator, calculated in the same way, gives the result

$$\overline{f_1(\mathbf{s}\mathbf{D}f_1)} = \overline{(\mu_1 X + \mu_2 Y + \mu_3 Z)(\alpha\mu_1 + \beta\mu_2 + \gamma\mu_3)}$$
$$= \overline{(\mu_1\alpha + \mu_2\beta + \mu_3\gamma)^2}F$$
$$= \frac{\mu_1^2 + \mu_2^2 + \mu_3^3}{3}F = \frac{\mu^2}{3}F.$$

Finally the second term in the denominator gives

$$\overline{f_1} = \mu_1\overline{\alpha} + \mu_2\overline{\beta} + \mu_3\overline{\gamma} = 0.$$

Hence [25′] may be written

$$\overline{m}_f = \left(\frac{a_{11} + a_{22} + a_{33}}{3} + \frac{\mu^2}{3KT}\right)F.$$

As our final result we can state that again the polarizability is a linear function of $1/T$,

$$\alpha = \frac{a_{11} + a_{22} + a_{33}}{3} + \frac{\mu^2}{3KT}, \qquad [26]$$

not different from the expression for α involved in [19]. What we called α_0 in that equation proves to be one third of the sum of the three coefficients a_{11}, a_{22}, and a_{33} which define the ellipsoid we introduced to visualize the behavior of the dielectric distortion in a field of any direction with respect to the molecule. The only essential suppositions made are that the energy of the molecule in an electric field can be represented as a function of no higher than the second degree in the field components, and that we are only interested in that most important part of the mean moment which is proportional to the field intensity.

CHAPTER III

MEASUREMENTS OF POLARITY AND ITS CONNECTION WITH
CHEMICAL STRUCTURE

9. The Effect of Temperature and the Calculation of Electric Moments.

As a general formula for the polarizability we found in the preceding section

$$\alpha = \alpha_0 + \frac{\mu^2}{3KT}.$$

For practical purposes it is more convenient not to refer to the polarizability itself, but, as we did before, to introduce the molar polarization P, which differs from α by the universal factor $(4\pi/3)N$. If therefore α can be represented as above, the formula for P will be

$$P = \frac{4\pi}{3} N \left(\alpha_0 + \frac{\mu^2}{3KT} \right). \qquad [27]$$

Assuming the validity of the assumptions about the internal field made by Clausius and Mosotti, we found that P could be calculated from measurements of the dielectric constant ϵ and the density ρ by the formula

$$P = \frac{\epsilon - 1}{\epsilon + 2} \frac{M}{\rho}.$$

But we emphasized that the validity of those assumptions is doubtful. That is why measurements of the dielectric constant of *gases* and *vapors* are important, for in this case the mutual interaction may be neglected and there is no doubt that we are allowed to calculate the molar polarization by the formula

$$P = \frac{\epsilon - 1}{3} \frac{M}{\rho}. \qquad [28]$$

All the measurements to be referred to in the present section have been made for vapors.

The first question is to determine whether a molecule is polar or non-polar. To decide this by the most straightforward method the dielectric constant ϵ and the density ρ have to be measured at different temperatures. Then P is calculated according to [28] and plotted as a function of the variable $1/T$. We expect two possibilities, illustrated by Figure 8: (1) P is not dependent on temperature at all. In this case the experiments are represented by a horizontal straight line. The molecule is non-polar, that is,

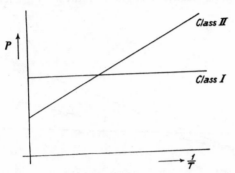

FIG. 8. Polarisation-temperature curves for polar (II) and nonpolar (I) substances.

its electric moment μ is, zero. (2) P depends on temperature. Plotting P as a function of $1/T$, we again expect a straight line in accordance with [27], but this time making a finite angle with the horizontal axis. In this case the molecule is polar, its electric moment having a finite value. Suppose that the experimental curve can be represented by the formula

$$P = a + \frac{b}{T},$$

with the two experimental constants a and b. Comparing this representation with [27], we infer that the molecule has an electric moment μ, which has to be calculated using the formula

$$\frac{4\pi}{9} \frac{N}{K} \mu^2 = b,$$

or substituting the values $N = 6.06 \times 10^{23}$ and $K = 1.37 \times 10^{-16}$ we find

$$\mu = 0.0127 \sqrt{b} \times 10^{-18}, \qquad [29]$$

in electrostatic units. This value we consider as the appropriate absolute measure of the polarity. For instance in the case of NH_3 Jona found $a = 5.45$ cc. and $b = 15250$ cc., giving $\mu = 1.57 \times 10^{-18}$ electrostatic units. All measurements have given moments of the order of magnitude 10^{-18} electrostatic units, which was to be expected in view of the fact that the moment, having the dimensions of charge times length, will be roughly the magnitude of the electronic charge (4.77×10^{-10}) times the molecular dimension (order of 10^{-8} cm.).

As an example of molecules which we would expect from the outset to be polar Figure 9 is given, representing measurements of

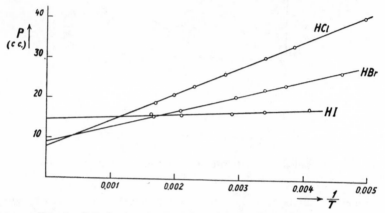

FIG. 9.   Polarisation-temperature curves for the hydrogen halides.

the temperature effect made by Zahn on HCl, HBr, and HI.   In fact we know, in this case, that in water solution the molecules split up into two oppositely charged ions, and we feel confident that also in the free molecule a remaining electric dissymmetry will exist. This fact is borne out by Figure 9, the electric moments as derived from these measurements being given in Table IV (p. 40).

Some remarks have to be made here in connection with the constant a, representing the unvariable part of the molar polarization.   This constant is $(4\pi/3)N\alpha_0$, and, as shown in Section 8, α_0 is equal to $(a_{11} + a_{22} + a_{33})/3$.   Now the larger these characteristic constants of the ellipsoid of distortion are, the larger will be the electric moment due to the elasticity of the molecule.   If, therefore, the whole polarization would have to be explained in the classical way, by distortion alone, we would have expected a molar polarization ranging from smaller to larger values in the series HCl, HBr, HI.   At ordinary temperature the arrangement is just the reverse, but if we extrapolate the straight lines in Figure 8 to very high temperatures, that is, until they cut the vertical axis, we really find the arrangement HCl, HBr, HI.   From our point of view this behavior is natural, since only for high temperatures the distortion part of the molar polarization is preponderant, whereas for ordinary temperatures the differences existing in the elasticity of the molecules are overcompensated by the orientation effect.

Another example for a series of gases containing non-polar and polar molecules is illustrated in Figure 10, representing the measurements of Sänger of the five gases CH_4, CH_3Cl, CH_2Cl_2, $CHCl_3$, and CCl_4. Whereas CH_4 and CCl_4 are non-polar, the three other mole-

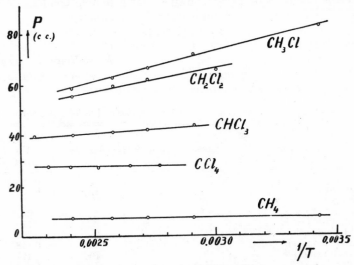

Fig. 10. Polar and nonpolar substituted methane compounds.

cules are decidedly polar; their electric moments are given in Table IV (p. 40).

Starting with the ordinary picture of the valencies of the C atom as directed towards the corners of a regular tetrahedron, we would indeed expect the result actually found experimentally. This example shows that an intimate connection exists between the temperature effect and the formula for the structure derived from chemical considerations, and we may hope that occasions will occur in which the dielectric method will prove to be of some help to decide whether a more or less dissymmetrical chemical formula has to be adopted for the substance.[1]

An interesting investigation of Smyth and Zahn concerning the influence of a double or triple bond between C atoms on the dissymmetry of the molecule should be mentioned at this place.[2]

The temperature effects for ethane (CH_3-CH_3), ethylene $(CH_2=CH_2)$, acetylene $(CH\equiv CH)$ and α-butylene $(CH_2=CH$

[1] An attempt to make a quantitative connection between the geometrical arrangement of atoms in the chemical formula and the dissymmetry as measured by the electric moment has been made by C. P. Smyth and S. O. Morgan, *J. Am. Chem. Soc.*, **49**, 1030 (1927), and by K. Höjendahl, *Nature*, **117**, 892 (1926), following the suggestion of J. J. Thomson, *Phil. Mag.*, **45**, 513 (1923). It seems probable that as soon as more measurements are available, in the majority of cases it will be possible to set up the moment from approximately constant vectorial contributions of the different groups constituting the molecule.

[2] C. P. Smyth and C. T. Zahn, *J. Am. Chem. Soc.*, **47**, 2501 (1925).

$-CH_2-CH_3$) were measured. The first three gases did not show any change of P with temperature, proving that their molecules are non-polar although they are unsaturated. The α-butylene, however, is found to be polar, showing that a double bond in an unsymmetrical position creates electrical dissymmetry.

In Table IV the electric moments so far measured for gases, using the temperature effect, have been collected. The letters refer to the observers: B = Baedeker, J = Jona, W = Weigt, Z = Zahn, Sm = Smyth, S = Sänger, St = Stuart, Br = von Braunmühl, Wa = Watson. The references are given below.[3]

TABLE IV. *Electric Moments of Molecules Measured in the Gaseous State.*

Substance	Chemical Formula	Observer	Electrostatic Units $(\mu) \times 10^{18}$
Argon	A	Br.	0
Hydrogen	H_2	Br.	0
Nitrogen	N_2	Z.	0
Hydrochloric acid	HCl	Z.	1.03
Hydrobromic acid	HBr	Z.	0.78
Hydroiodic acid	HI	Z.	0.38
Carbon monoxide	CO	W.	0.118
Carbon monoxide	CO	Br.	0.124
Water	H_2O	J.	1.87
Hydrogen sulfide	H_2S	Br.	1.10
Sulfur dioxide	SO_2	B.	1.60
Sulfur dioxide	SO_2	J.	1.76
Sulfur dioxide	SO_2	Z.	1.61
Nitrous oxide	N_2O	Br.	0.249
Carbon dioxide	CO_2	J.	0.3
Carbon dioxide	CO_2	W.	0.142
Carbon dioxide	CO_2	Z.	0.06
Carbon dioxide	CO_2	Br.	0.145
Carbon dioxide	CO_2	St.	0.00
Ammonia	NH_3	J.	1.53
Ammonia	NH_3	Z.	1.44
Ammonia	NH_3	Wa.	1.46–1.51
Phosphine	PH_3	Wa.	0.54–0.56
Arsine	AsH_3	Wa.	0.13–0.18
Methane	CH_4	S.	0
Methyl chloride	CH_3Cl	S.	1.97
Dichlor-methane	CH_2Cl_2	S.	1.59
Chloroform	$CHCl_3$	S.	0.95
Carbon tetrachloride	CCl_4	S.	0
Ethane	CH_3-CH_3	Sm.a.Z.	0
Ethene	$CH_2=CH_2$	Sm.a.Z.	0
Acetylene	$CH\equiv CH$	Sm.a.Z.	0
α-Butylene	$CH_2=C_3H_6$	Sm.a.Z.	0.37
Ethyl ether	$C_2H_5-O-C_2H_5$	S.	0.99
Ethyl alcohol	C_2H_5OH	S.	1.1

[3] K. Baedeker, *Z. physik. Chem.*, **36**, 305 (1901); M. Jona, *Physik. Z.*, **20**, 14 (1919); H. Weigt, *Physik. Z.*, **22**, 643 (1921); C. T. Zahn, *Phys. Rev.*, **24**, 400 (1924); C. P. Smyth and C. T. Zahn, *J. Am. Chem. Soc.*, **47**, 2501 (1925); C. T. Zahn, *Phys. Rev.*, **27**, 455 (1926); R. Sänger, *Physik. Z.*, **27**, 556 (1926); **28**, 455 (1927); H. v. Braunmühl, *Physik. Z.*, **28**, 141 (1927); H. E. Watson, *Proc. Royal Soc.* [A], **117**, 43 (1927); H. A. Stuart, *Z. Physik.*, **47**, 457 (1928).

The molecules of simple constitution contained in this table still deserve some remarks. The monatomic argon and the molecules H_2 and N_2 consisting of two identical atoms are non-polar. If, however, two different atoms like C and O in CO are combined, the result is a slight dissymmetry. All triatomic molecules mentioned have permanent moments, with the exception of CO_2, as is definitely shown by Stuart.[4] This shows that the atoms as in H_2O or SO_2, for instance, cannot be situated in a symmetrical linear arrangement. Considerations relating to the interatomic forces, to be represented in Chapter IV, will lead to a triangular arrangement and will also elucidate in a similar way the strong dissymmetry observed for the NH_3 molecule. From the point of view of the organic chemist this electric dissymmetry is in striking accordance with the hypothesis put forward by Hantzsch and Werner [5] in order to explain the stereoisomerism of carbon-nitrogen compounds as, for instance, aldoximes and ketoximes by the assumption that the three valencies of the N atom are not directed in one plane.

As for the measurements themselves, from which the moments of Table IV have been derived, many have been made at different temperatures but at constant pressure. In this way the gas can expand, and the densities for different temperatures must be known. The method used by Sänger, in which the density is kept constant at different temperatures, does away with the reduction to constant density and is perhaps to be preferred. It certainly shows the existence of the temperature effect in its most characteristic form, as we are dealing with an invariable number of molecules per cc. and nevertheless find a decrease of the electric moment set up in every cc. with increasing temperature.

Departures from the linear relation connecting P and $1/T$ may be expected for lower temperatures or higher densities as soon as the mutual interaction of the molecules becomes of practical importance. So far some deviations found in this direction by Jona do not seem to be beyond doubt. Zahn [6] is inclined to attribute the deviations observed by Jona to adsorption on the plates of the condenser. However, deviations due to real association must exist, and as soon as reliable measurements are available some interesting conclusions as to the magnitude and direction of the forces causing association will be possible.[7] On the other hand high temperatures may change

---

[4] E. F. Barker, *Astrophys. J.*, **55**, 391 (1922); D. M. Dennison, *Phil. Mag.*, [7] **1**, 195 (1926); Cl. Schaefer and B. Philipp, *Z. Physik.*, **36**, 641 (1926); A. Eucken, *Z. Physik.*, **37**, 714 (1926); N. Stark and O. Blüh, *Physik. Z.*, **28**, 502 (1927); Cl. Schaefer, *Physik. Z.*, **28**, 667 (1927); K. L. Wolff, *Z. physik. Chem.*, **131**, 90 (1927); H. A. Stuart, *Z. Physik.*, **47**, 457 (1928).

[5] A. Hantzsch and A. Werner, *Ber.*, **23**, 11 (1890); *compare also* Chap. III, p. 197, in A. W. Stewart, "Stereochemistry," Longmans, Green & Co., 1907.

[6] C. T. Zahn, *Phys. Rev.*, **27**, 329 (1926).

[7] Recent measurements of F. Maske, *Physik. Z.*, **28**, 533 (1927), seem to indicate association of the expected nature in vapor of Benzophenon at lower temperature.

the distances between the nuclei to some extent and cause a varia
tion of the electric moment itself.

10. Molar Polarization and Molar Refraction. Second Method for the Measurement of Polarity.

If we consider again the fundamental formula for the molar
polarization

$$P = \frac{4\pi}{3} N \left(\alpha_0 + \frac{\mu^2}{3KT} \right),$$

it is obvious that a method for measuring only the part $(4\pi/3)N\alpha_0$,
which we will call P_0, would enable us to dispense with measurements on the temperature effect in order to determine μ. One
measurement of P at any temperature, combined with the supposed
measurement of P_0 by another method, would enable us to calculate
μ by the formula

$$\frac{4\pi}{3} \frac{N\mu^2}{3KT} = P - P_0,$$

or substituting $N = 6.06 \times 10^{23}$ and $K = 1.37 \times 10^{-16}$

$$\mu = 0.0127 \times 10^{-18} \sqrt{(P - P_0)T}. \qquad [30]$$

Now we have to expect that for high enough frequencies the
orientation effect will not exist, and this is indeed a result which will
be derived for liquids in Chapter IV and for gases in Chapter X.
Therefore, confining our attention still to gases and vapors alone, if
we calculate the expression

$$\frac{r^2 - 1}{3} \frac{M}{\rho},$$

introducing the square of the refraction index r instead of ϵ, we will
have found a value for P_0. But this value is the optical polarization
corresponding to the special frequency ν for which the measurement
of r has been made, and is essentially dependent on ν. The polarization by distortion P_0 entering in [30] is another quantity; it would be
possible to define this quantity as the limiting value that the optical
polarization attains on passing to the limit for the frequency $\nu = 0$,
when the orientation effect which will set in for smaller frequencies
is disregarded. Unfortunately, this extrapolation can hardly be
carried out accurately using the dispersion measurements now at
our disposal. Therefore [30] cannot be used when absolute accuracy is necessary. Nevertheless from a practical standpoint
this aspect is entirely changed. Suppose we take *non-polar*
molecules and compare the value of the dielectric constant with the
square of the refraction index for some definite frequency in the

visible spectrum. Practically the difference between ϵ and r^2 is often found to be small, in reality due to the fact that usually the natural frequencies which cause the dispersion are far in the ultra-violet. As an example Table V contains some values of $\epsilon - 1$ and $r^2 - 1$ for a number of non-polar gases, measured at atmospheric pressure and at 0° centigrade. The values given in Table V are

TABLE V. *Dielectric Constant and Refraction.*

Substance	$(\epsilon - 1) \times 10^3$	$(r^2 - 1) \times 10^3$
H_2	0.26	0.28
N_2	0.61	0.59
O_2	0.55	0.54
CH_4	0.94	0.88
C_2H_6	1.31	1.51

taken from Landolt-Börnstein tables, the refraction index referring to light of the sodium *D*-line.

If now we feel confident that an agreement of the same kind will occur for other cases and for polar molecules, we would expect to get a good approximation in calculating P_0 by means of the formula

$$P_0 = \frac{r^2 - 1}{3} \frac{M}{\rho}, \qquad [31]$$

where r is the ordinary refraction index.

Using a dispersion formula of the ordinary type, the attempt could be made to perform the extrapolations to zero frequency. But in general the polar molecules, in which we are primarily interested, show not only absorption in the ultra-violet but also in the infra-red part of the spectrum. Part of this dispersion is due to the permanent moment itself and should not be taken into account. Another part however, which has to be considered, is due to vibrations of the atomic masses in the molecular system, an instance being the well-known bands of HCl which give evidence of the superposition of the quantum rotation on the vibration. Therefore we are apt to make a more appreciable error in the case of polar molecules if we use the ordinary optical refraction index for the calculation of P_0. Practically speaking, even this error is generally small, the calculation with the help of [31] giving a fair approximation.

It would be advisable if in further calculations of the moment by the help of [30] a general agreement was adopted as to the wave length for which r shall be taken. We will constantly use the wave length of the sodium *D*-line, for which many refraction measurements have been carried out.

Let us consider the molecule NH_3 as an example. According to Jona's measurements of the dielectric constant, the molar polarization P at the temperature $T = 292.2$ is 57.6 cc. (*compare* Table III, p. 20). On the other hand the index of refraction for $T = 273$ is given in Landolt-Börnstein tables as $r = 1.000379$ for sodium *D*-light. Treating NH_3 as an ideal gas, for which at this temperature the molal volume $(M/\rho) = 22.4 \times 10^3$, we find

$$P_0 = \frac{r^2 - 1}{3} \frac{M}{\rho} = 5.7 \text{ cc.,}$$

and this optical polarization does not change with temperature. Substituting in [30] $P - P_0 = 51.9$ and $T = 292.2$, we find

$$\mu = 1.56 \times 10^{-18} \text{ e.s.u.}$$

In Table IV the value of the moment derived by Jona from experiments on the temperature variation was $\mu = 1.53 \times 10^{-18}$, and our second method therefore proves to be very satisfactory. NH_3 is a case in which the difference $P - P_0 = 51.9$ is relatively large compared with $P_0 = 5.7$. That is why a moderate mistake in P_0 will not be serious. If however the molecule is only slightly polar, then the difference $P - P_0$ will be much more affected by an error in P_0 and the second method is much less satisfactory. Therefore this method, although good enough for the calculation of the moment of decidedly polar molecules, is not well adapted to decide if a molecule is slightly polar or non-polar at all. Practically it serves very well to distinguish polar from non-polar gases qualitatively, for if ϵ differs appreciably from r^2, or what amounts to the same if $\epsilon - 1$ is appreciably larger than $2(r - 1)$, the molecule is polar.

11. Second Method Applied to Solutions.

So far we have confined our attention to gases and vapors. Suppose now that a solution has been made of polar molecules in a solvent which is known to be non-polar. For small concentrations the dissolved molecules will be far apart in the average, and the only interaction of importance will be between the polar molecules and the surrounding non-polar molecules of the solvent. In this case it is probable that the interaction can be expressed adopting Mosotti's assumption about the internal field. If we assume this, the method of Section 10 can be generalized to cover experiments made on dilute binary mixtures, and in this way measurements of polarity become very simple.

Let us start with the assumption that Mosotti's calculation can be applied for all concentrations, although this assumption will ultimately be used only for the limiting case of diluted solutions. If then α_1 is the polarizability of a molecule of the first component and α_2 of a molecule of the second component, and if n_1 and n_2 represent the numbers of molecules present in 1 cc., we have

$$\frac{\epsilon - 1}{\epsilon + 2} = \frac{4\pi}{3}(n_1\alpha_1 + n_2\alpha_2).$$

Introducing the mole fractions

$$f_1 = \frac{n_1}{n_1 + n_2}, \qquad f_2 = \frac{n_2}{n_1 + n_2},$$

and the molar polarizations

$$P_1 = \frac{4\pi}{3} N\alpha_1, \qquad P_2 = \frac{4\pi}{3} N\alpha_2,$$

the relation takes the form

$$\frac{\epsilon - 1}{\epsilon + 2} \frac{M_1 f_1 + M_2 f_2}{\rho} = P_1 f_1 + P_2 f_2, \qquad [32]$$

where the density is denoted by ρ and M_1 and M_2 are the molecular weights of the two components.

The density is represented by the expression

$$\rho = \frac{n_1 M_1 + n_2 M_2}{N}.$$

The substitution of

$$n_1 = f_1(n_1 + n_2), \qquad n_2 = f_2(n_1 + n_2),$$

leads to the result

$$\frac{\epsilon - 1}{\epsilon + 2} \frac{1}{\rho} = \frac{n_1 + n_2}{n_1 M_1 + n_2 M_2} \frac{4\pi}{3} N(f_1 \alpha_1 + f_2 \alpha_2).$$

Multiplying both sides by

$$\frac{n_1 M_1 + n_2 M_2}{n_1 + n_2} = f_1 M_1 + f_2 M_2,$$

and remembering the definitions of the molar polarizations P_1 and P_2, equation [32] is obtained at once.

The right hand side of [32] we will call the molar polarization of the mixture and denote by P_{12}; equation [32] states how this molar polarization can be calculated for a mixture assuming the validity of Mosotti's assumption.

We now consider the dependence of P_{12} on the concentration at a given constant temperature, using as abscissae the mole fractions. If we take for the constituent 1 a non-polar substance and for the constituent 2 a polar substance, and fix our attention on the left hand part of the curves, corresponding to dilute solutions of component 2 in the solvent 1, three types of curves for P_{12} are possible as illustrated by Figures 11, 12, and 13. These figures represent the molar polarization of the mixtures ethyl alcohol-benzene, ethyl ether-benzene and nitrobenzene-benzene, where benzene is to be considered as a non-polar substance.[8]

[8] R. Sänger, *Physik. Z.*, **27**, 165 (1926).

For small concentrations of the solute 2 the change in the molar polarization P_{12} is always proportional to the mole fraction f_2, as indicated by the tangent drawn to the curves. For higher concentra-

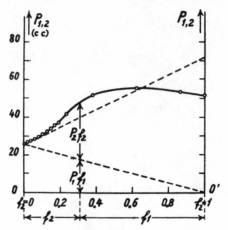

Fig. 11. Variation of Polarisation for mixtures of Ethyl alcohol-Benzene
(2)   (1)

tions the three substances behave in a different manner. In type I the curve bends upward such that if we would represent it by the formula

$$P_{12} = \beta + \gamma f_2 + \delta f_2^2$$

the coefficient δ is positive. In type II P_{12} is represented by a straight line over the whole range of concentrations, the curve and

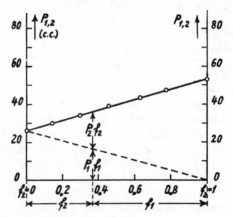

Fig. 12. Variation of Polarisation for mixtures of Ethyl ether-Benzene (18° C.)
(2)   (1)

tangent being coincident, and the coefficient δ zero. In type III the curve bends downwards such that the coefficient δ would be negative.

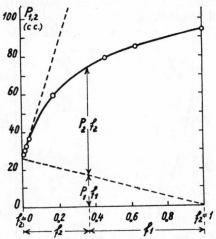

FIG. 13. Variation of Polarisation for mixtures of Nitrobenzene-Benzene.

(2) (1)

The significance of these different curvatures can be brought out more clearly by considering the two terms of P_{12}.

$$P_{12} = P_1 f_1 + P_2 f_2.$$

The index 1 refers to the non-polar solvent and P_1 may be considered as a constant throughout. If then we draw a straight line beginning at the point where the curve starts at the left hand side and ending at the right hand origin ($f_1 = 0$, $f_2 = 1$), the ordinates of this

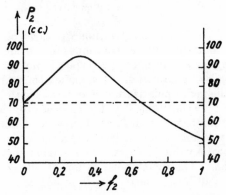

FIG. 14. Polarisation-concentration curve for Ethyl alcohol.

straight line will represent P_1f_1. The vertical distance between this
straight line and the curve will represent P_2f_2 as a function of the
mole fraction f_2 of the polar constituent. Dividing this distance by
the corresponding abscissa f_2, the molar polarization P_2 of the polar
molecule itself is obtained. Figures 14 and 15 represent P_2 for
ethyl alcohol and nitrobenzene as a function of the mole fraction f_2.

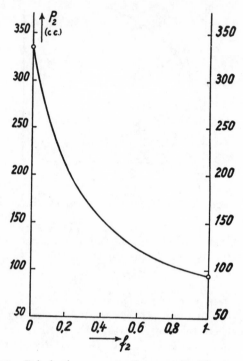

Fig. 15.   Polarisation-concentration curve for Nitrobenzene.

For type I the molar polarization P_2 starts of course with a
finite value for infinitely diluted solutions ($f_2 = 0$) but first *increases*
with increasing concentration.   For type II (not represented by a
curve) the molar polarization P_2 remains constant throughout.
For type III the molar polarization P_2 *decreases* with increasing concentration.   Of special interest is the case of ethyl alcohol, whose
molar polarization begins with 72 cc., increases to a maximum value
of 96 cc., finally decreasing for still higher concentrations and reaching
in pure alcohol the value 52 cc., which is smaller than the value for
infinite dilution.   The molar polarization of nitrobenzene, on the
other hand, is continually decreasing from 334 cc. to 94 cc. in pure
nitrobenzene.

The discussion of these changes in the molar polarization of polar molecules with their concentration throws some light on the association process which goes on in such solutions.[9] Here however we are only concerned with the limiting value of P_2 which is reached for $f_2 = 0$; that is, for infinitely diluted solutions, because this represents the molar polarization of a free polar molecule not in interaction with any other polar molecules of the same kind. By carrying out the construction we described, or making the corresponding calculation, the molar polarization of free molecules can be found. If from now on we drop the index, the only thing left is to combine this value of P with the optical value P_0, calculated from the refraction index r of the pure polar liquid as

$$P_0 = \frac{r^2 - 1}{r^2 + 2} \frac{M}{\rho},$$

and to find the electric moment, applying equation [30]:

$$\mu = 0.0127 \times 10^{-18} \sqrt{(P - P_0)T}.$$

This method was first used by Miss Lange,[10] and has recently been applied by Errera [11] and by Williams.[12] Measurements of the dielectric constant of binary mixtures have of course been made several times, as for instance long ago by J. C. Philipp.[13] But only recently have such measurements been discussed from the point of view of the dipole theory.

Table VI contains the moments which have been determined in this way by Williams at 25° C. from measurements on solutions in four different non-polar solvents: benzene (C_6H_6), carbon tetrachloride (CCl_4), carbon disulfide (CS_2), and hexane (C_6H_{14}). There may exist some doubt if carbon disulfide really is a non-polar solvent, but the experiments show that if a moment of the CS_2-molecule exists it certainly is so small that it has not to be taken in account within the limits of precision of the method described in this section.

An intimate connection with the structural formula is evident at once. Carbon tetrachloride (CCl_4) proves again to be non-polar consistent with Sänger's measurements on the temperature effect in the vapor state. The same is true for the four substances used as

[9] Compare P. Debye in "Handbuch der Radiologie," Vol. 6, p. 633. An excellent discussion of the general principles involved has also been published by L. Ebert, Z. physik. Chem., **113**, 1 (1924); **114**, 430 (1924).
[10] L. Lange, Z. Physik., **33**, 169 (1925), Diss. Göttingen, 1918.
[11] J. Errera, Physik. Z., **27**, 764 (1926).
[12] I. J. W. Williams and I. J. Krchma, J. Am. Chem. Soc., **49**, 1676 (1927); II. I. J. Krchma and J. W. Williams, ibid., **49**, 2408 (1927); III. J. W. Williams and R. T. Allgeier, ibid., **49**, 2416, 1927; IV. J. W. Williams and E. F. Ogg, ibid., **50**, 94 (1928); V. J. W. Williams and C. H. Schwingel, ib d., **50**, 362 (1928).
[13] J. C. Philipp, Z. physik. Chem., **24**, 18 (1897).

solvents, for if carbon disulphide dissolved in benzene is considered, for instance, the molar polarization is $P = 22.2$ cc., whereas the optical polarization is $P_0 = 21.1$ cc. From the difference $P - P_0 = 1.1$ cc. a moment of 0.06×10^{-18} electrostatic unit can be calculated, but this small difference is certainly within the limits of precision of the method, as has been said before, considering the possible precision of the value for the optical polarization P_0.

TABLE VI. *Electric Moments of Molecules Measured in Solution.*

(a) *Solvent—Benzene*

Molecule	Article *	P(cc.)	P_0(cc.)	$P-P_0$(cc.)	Electro-static Units $(\mu)\times 10^{18}$
Toluene..................	I	36.3	30.3	6.0	0.52
o-xylene..................	I	40.8	35.0	5.8	0.52
p-xylene..................	I	36.7	35.5	1.2	0.06
Nitrobenzene..............	V	348	32.0	316	3.90
o-Dinitrobenzene...........	V	800	35	765	6.05
m-Dinitrobenzene...........	V	338	35	303	3.81
p-Dinitrobenzene...........	V	37.0	34	3	0.32
1-3-5-Trinitrobenzene.......	V	64.5	40	24.5	1.08
o-Nitrotoluene.............	V	331	38	293	3.75
m-Nitrotoluene.............	V	407	38	369	4.20
p-Nitrotoluene.............	V	463	38	425	4.50
Benzoic acid..............	III	43.5	24.6	18.9	1.0
Phenol...................	III	89.0	27.7	61.3	1.70
Chlorobenzene.............	I	82.0	31.0	51.0	1.52
Hexane...................	IV	30.5	29.6	0.9	0.05
Carbon disulfide...........	IV	22.2	21.1	1.1	0.06
Chloroform...............	I	47.5	21.3	26.2	1.10
Carbon tetrachloride........	I	28.2	28.3	—	0.00
Ethyl ether...............	I	54.5	23.0	31.5	1.22
Iodine...................	III	60.2	20.0	40.2	1.4
Stannic iodide.............	III	26.7	30	—	0
Silver perchlorate..........	III	477.0	16	461.0	4.70

TABLE VI. *(Continued)*

(b) *Solvent—Carbon tetrachloride*

Molecule	Article *	P(cc.)	P_0(cc.)	$P-P_0$(cc.)	Electro-static Units $(\mu)\times 10^{18}$
Benzene..................	II	26.7	25.8	0.9	0.06
Toluene..................	II	33.7	30.3	3.4	0.40
Chloroform...............	II	49.8	21.3	28.5	1.15
Ethyl ether...............	II	56.0	23.0	33.0	1.24
Methyl acetate.............	II	78.0	18.0	60.0	1.67
Ethyl acetate..............	II	87.0	22.2	64.8	1.74
Acetone..................	II	170.0	16.0	154.0	2.70
Ethyl alcohol..............	II	73.5	16.0	57.5	1.63
iso-Amyl alcohol...........	II	86.0	13.0	73.0	1.85

(c) Solvent—Carbon disulfide

Molecule	Article *	P(cc.)	P_0(cc.)	$P-P_0$(cc.)	Electrostatic Units $(\mu)\times 10^{-18}$
Benzene	IV	28.5	25.8	2.7	0.1
Nitrobenzene	IV	346.0	32.0	314.0	3.89
Phenol	IV.	83.6	27.5	56.1	1.63
Chlorobenzene	IV	82.5	31.0	51.5	1.52
Naphthalene	IV	54.0	43.5	10.5	0.69
Hexane	IV	31.6	29.6	2.0	0.08

(d) Solvent—Hexane

Molecule	Article *	P(cc.)	P_0(cc.)	$P-P_0$(cc.)	Electrostatic Units $(\mu)\times 10^{-18}$
Benzene	IV	27.8	25.8	2.0	0.08
Nitrobenzene	IV	346.0	32.0	314.0	3.89
Chlorobenzene	IV	84.0	31.0	53.0	1.55
Naphthalene	IV	55.0	43.5	11.5	0.72
Carbon disulfide	IV.	23.1	21.1	2.0	0.08

* See note 12, p. 49.

The monosubstituents of benzene are all dissymmetrical, as is shown in Table VI for toluene ($C_6H_5CH_3$), nitrobenzene ($C_6H_5NO_2$), benzoic acid (C_6H_5COOH), phenol (C_6H_5OH), and chlorobenzene (C_6H_5Cl) in accordance with the arrangement of the atoms in the chemical formula. The amount of dissymmetry, however, is different for the different substituted groups; the effect increases in the order CH_3, COOH, Cl, OH, NO_2.

The effect of the substitution of two equal groups in the benzene molecule depends essentially on their geometrical arrangement. If they are in the ortho- or in the meta-position the resulting molecule is polar; in the para-position the effect is cancelled out as now the two groups act in opposite directions and the picture of the molecule is symmetrical. Examples are given in the table by the figures for the dinitrobenzenes [$C_6H_4(NO_2)_2$] and the xylenes [$C_6H_4(CH_3)_2$].[14]

If the two substituted groups are not equal, a moment even of the para-compound remains, as illustrated by the three nitrotoluenes ($C_6H_4CH_3NO_2$). If we compare the moment for the p-nitrotoluene with the moment of the nitrobenzene, we see that the first molecule

[14] Very recently, however, J. W. Williams, Physik. Z., 29, 683 (1928), could show that this does not hold always. The substance derived from Hydrochinon [$C_6H_4(OH)_2$], by replacing the two H-atoms of the OH-groups by C_2H_5, is decidedly polar. It is suggested that the sidegroups are not situated in the plane of the benzene-ring.

has the larger moment, although the CH_3-group and the NO_2-group are at the opposite ends of the molecule. If now we consider a molecule like CH_3Cl, I think we may be willing to consider the CH_3-part as carrying an excess of positive charge and the Cl-part as being negatively charged. In the same sense we may locate an excess of negative charge in the NO_2-group also, as being analogous to Cl. Accepting this, it is at once evident why the substitution of an NO_2-group in para-position to the CH_3-group does not decrease but increases the total moment of the molecule. Appropriate measurements of the polarity can therefore be used to determine the electropositive or electronegative character of groups.

The moment found for the 1-3-5-trinitrobenzene is very interesting. A plane formula of this molecule would be symmetrical. To explain the dissymmetry it would be possible to assume a benzene ring with its carbon atoms arranged in two planes in the same way as the atoms have been arranged in diamond by Bragg. We have, however, the other possibility that the NO_2-groups are not situated in the plane of the benzene-ring. It must be said that the calculated moment for the trinitrobenzene is fairly large and corresponds to a difference $P - P_0$ which is 37 per cent of the total polarization. From this we should infer that the moment is indeed significant. We know, however, that the method of this section can give only approximate results. Definite conclusions should therefore be suspended till measurements of the temperature-effect for diluted solutions of the substance in a non-polar solvent will be available.

An analogous remark has to be made with respect to the moment found for naphthalene ($C_{10}H_8$) and for iodine (I_2). From the existence of some compounds containing iodine the conclusion may be drawn that the I-atom can form a cation as well as an anion. Hence it would not be impossible that the I_2-molecule ultimately is dissymmetrical. The case certainly deserves further careful examination.

Considering the chemical formula, it is not astonishing that methyl and ethyl acetate or acetone prove to be dissymmetrical

$$
\begin{array}{ccc}
\overset{\displaystyle O}{\underset{\displaystyle }{\overset{\|}{C}}} & \overset{\displaystyle O}{\underset{\displaystyle }{\overset{\|}{C}}} & \overset{\displaystyle O}{\underset{\displaystyle }{\overset{\|}{C}}} \\
CH_3 \quad OCH_3 \qquad \text{and} \qquad CH_3 \quad OC_2H_5 \qquad \text{or} \qquad CH_3 \quad CH_3
\end{array}
$$

and the same is true for chloroform ($CHCl_3$) and for the alcohols. The table contains ethyl- and iso-amyl alcohol. Miss Lange (loc. cit.) has measured besides $\mu = 1.53 \times 10^{-18}$ for propyl alcohol and 1.65×10^{-18} for butyl alcohol. The characteristic OH-group seems therefore to create a moment, which does not depend very appreciably on the constitution of the rest of the molecule.

Ethyl ether ($C_2H_5OC_2H_5$) is analogous to water (HOH); its moment is presumably due to a triangular arrangement of the oxygen-atom and the two ethyl-groups. The dissymmetry of silver perchlorate ($AgClO_4$) is of course to be expected. The non-polar character of the stannic iodide (SnI_4) may be taken as an indication that the four I-atoms are situated at the corners of a tetrahedron analogous to the four H-atoms in methane (CH_4).

During the last years Errera has made important contributions to the question of the connection between the dissymmetry as derived from the dielectric properties of the molecule and its chemical formula. He uses again our formula [30] for the calculation of the moment, but in some cases prefers another method to determine the value of P_0. Instead of using the refractive index, he measures the dielectric constant in the solid state and considers the molar polarization in this state as P_0, calculating this with the help of the formula

$$P_0 = \frac{\epsilon - 1}{\epsilon + 2} \frac{M}{\rho},$$

in which ϵ now refers to the solid state. He shows for instance how the substitution of two Cl-atoms in the benzene-ring produces moments in the ortho- and the meta-grouping but not in the para-grouping. In another paper he treats the isomers of the dichloro-ethylene, which are represented by the formula

$$\begin{array}{cc} H & H \\ C = C \\ Cl & Cl \end{array}, \qquad \begin{array}{cc} H & Cl \\ C = C \\ Cl & H \end{array}, \qquad \begin{array}{cc} Cl & H \\ C = C \\ Cl & H \end{array}.$$

For the first (cis) form and the last (asymmetrical) form the electric moments $\mu = 1.89 \times 10^{-18}$ and $\mu = 1.18 \times 10^{-18}$ are found, whereas the second (trans) form is non-polar in accordance with the geometrical picture adopted in organic chemistry.[15]

Another interesting application has recently been made by L. Ebert in order to determine if the valencies of the C-atom have always to be taken as directed to the corners of a tetrahedron. According to Weissenberg [16] the possibility should be discussed that those valencies may sometimes point to the four corners of a regular tetragonal pyramid with the C-atom at the top. The evidence drawn from crystal analysis does not seem to be quite conclusive at this time; moreover in a crystal the molecules cannot be considered as free. Ebert has therefore measured the molar polarization of

[15] J. Errera and M. Lepingle, *Acad. Royale Belgique*, p. 150, 192⁻; J. Errera, *Acad. Royale Belgique*, p. 154, 1925; *J. phys.*, **6**, 390 (1925); *Physik. Z.*, **27**, 769 (1926).
[16] K. Weissenberg, *Physik. Z.*, **28**, 829 (1927) (This article contains references to the former literature).

diluted appropriate solutions of some compounds in which the central C-atom is connected with four equal groups and reports that among them he has found molecules with a permanent moment. It follows according to Ebert from this result that sometimes the valencies of the C-atom cannot be represented using the classical tetrahedron. To date the results are published in a preliminary note only.[17]

In another note Ebert [18] has applied the method described in this section to determine the form in which the undissociated molecules of acids occur.

A last question may be put forward here, namely the question whether the electric moment of a polar molecule in a non-polar liquid will be independent of the solvent and the same as the moment of the absolutely free molecule. As the internal forces which control the distances of the atoms in the compound are of electric origin, we should perhaps expect a small difference to exist, increasing with increasing dielectric constant of the non-polar solvent. Table VII

TABLE VII. *Electric Moments Measured in Different Solvents.*

Molecule	Solvent	P	P_0	$P-P_0$	Electrostatic Units $(\mu) \times 10^{-18}$
Benzene*.............	CCl$_4$	26.7	25.8	0.9	0.06
	CS$_2$	28.5	25.8	2.7	0.10
	C$_r$H$_{14}$	27.8	25.8	2.0	0.08
Nitrobenzene........	C$_r$H$_6$	348	32.0	316	3.90
	CS$_2$	346	32.0	314	3.89
	C$_r$H$_{14}$	346	32.0	314	3.89
Chlorobenzene......	C H$_6$	82.0	31.0	51.0	1.52
	CS$_2$	82.5	31.0	51.5	1.52
	C$_6$H$_{14}$	84.0	31.0	53.0	1.55
Naphthalene........	CS$_2$	54.0	43.5	10.5	0.69
	C$_6$H$_{14}$	55.0	43.5	11.5	0.72
Ethyl ether.........	C H$_6$	54.5	23.0	31.5	1.22
	CCl$_4$	56.0	23.0	33.0	1.24

* The calculated values of μ for benzene are to be considered as 0 within the limits of precision.

contains the data for those molecules which have been measured by Williams and his co-workers in different solvents. It is obvious that within the limits of precision attained in these measurements no such difference occurs. On the other hand the values for the moments of ethyl ether and ethyl alcohol lately published by Sänger (*compare* Table IV) are both smaller than the values of Williams for the same substances. As Sänger made his measurements in

[17] L. Ebert, *Naturwissenschaften*, **15**, 669 (1927).
[18] L. Ebert, *Ibid.*, **13**, 681 (1925).

the vapor state and Williams in solutions, the difference might be real, however the precision of the measurements made for the gaseous state may not be as high as the figures seem to indicate. Therefore the experimental evidence now available does not warrant definite conclusion.

12. The Temperature Effect in Diluted Solutions.

Suppose that for a certain temperature the molar polarization P has been found using the method described in Section 11, which gives this value as it is for infinite dilution. According to the general theory this quantity should then be represented by the formula

$$P = \frac{4\pi}{3} N \left(\alpha_0 + \frac{\mu^2}{3KT} \right).$$

In Section 11 the attempt was made to calculate the moment μ using the value of ϵ measured at one single temperature, and introducing for $(4\pi/3)N\alpha_0 = P_0$ a value derived from measurements of the refraction-index. It is obvious that it would be very important as a test of the theory if it could be shown that for different temperatures the molar polarization P of polar molecules contained in a non-polar liquid is represented by our equation, and therefore is a linear function of $1/T$, as was already found for the gaseous state. Some measurements made by L. Lange (loc. cit.) on solutions of nitrobenzene in benzene or toluene, at different temperatures, can serve this purpose. From her curves we obtain by extrapolation the values contained in Table VIII for the molar polarization P of nitrobenzene, at the four different temperatures T for which experiments have been made.

TABLE VIII.   *Polarization of Nitrobenzene in Benzene at Different Temperatures.*

T	P	$P-P_0$	$(P-P_0)(T/300)$
297	346	313	310
318	312	279	296
338	296	263	296
373	271	238	296

The values of P decrease as they should with increasing temperature. The optical polarization P_0 was derived from measurements on the refractive index using the D-line, giving $P_0 = 33$ cc., and leaving the difference $P - P_0$ as due to orientation alone. This difference should now be proportional to $1/T$, as a test of which the product $(P - P_0)(T/300)$ was calculated (introducing the constant factor $1/300$ merely for convenience). Table VIII shows that, whereas $P - P_0$ changes from 313 to 238, the product of this quantity with $T/300$ remains indeed approximately constant.

The question has recently been taken up by C. P. Smyth and S. O. Morgan, who have measured the dielectric constants for solutions of chloroform ($CHCl_3$), monochlorobenzene (C_6H_5Cl) and ethyl bromide (C_2H_5Br) in the non-polar solvent hexane (C_6H_{14}). These investigators employed different concentrations and used the entire range of temperature for which the mixtures are liquid.[19] At each temperature the molar polarization P of the polar constituent was derived by extrapolating the concentration curve of P_{12} to zero concentration. (Compare Section 11.) The values for P found in this way are contained in Table IX and represented as a function of $1/T$ in Figure 16.

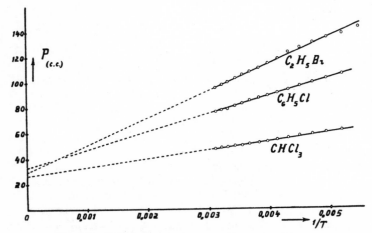

FIG. 16. Polarisation-temperature curves in solution.

TABLE IX. *Temperature Effect in Diluted Solutions.*

T	$CHCl_3$	C H Cl	C_2H_5Br
	cc.	cc.	cc.
183	—	—	143.5
193	62.1	106.5	138.5
203	60.2	103.0	135.0
213	58.9	100.0	131.0
223	57.5	97.0	127.0
233	56.0	94.0	123.5
243	54.6	91.0	118.5
253	53.1	89.3	114.3
263	52.3	87.5	111.0
273	51.1	85.5	107.9
283	50.0	83.5	105.5
293	49.7	81.5	103.3
303	48.8	79.0	100.2
313	48.3	77.8	97.6
323	47.5	76.8	95.4

[19] I owe it to the kindness of Dr. Smyth that I can present here his interesting results before they have been published in the usual way.

The figure shows that the molar polarization is indeed a linear function of $1/T$, the finite slope of the straight lines indicating that all three molecules are polar. If P is represented in the form

$$P = a + \frac{b}{T},$$

the coefficient b can serve to calculate the electric moment using equation [29]. Smyth [20] found $\mu\,(CHCl_3) = 1.05 \times 10^{-18}$, $\mu\,(C_6H_5Cl) = 1.52 \times 10^{-18}$ and $\mu\,(C_2H_5Br) = 1.86 \times 10^{-18}$. The constant a, appearing as the ordinate for $1/T = 0$, was calculated also, the values found for the three substances of Table VIII being 26.6 cc., 33.2 cc. and 29.5 cc., showing for instance that the molar polarization for free molecules of C_2H_5Br at $0°$ C., having the value 107.9 cc. (see Table IX), is composed of 29.5 cc. due to distortion and 78.4 cc. due to orientation of the molecule.

According to the theory the constant a is what we called P_0 and should not be very different from the molar refraction

$$P_0 = \frac{r^2 - 1}{r^2 + 1} \frac{M}{\rho}$$

of the pure polar substance, as discussed in the foregoing Section 11. Smyth extrapolated the molar refraction to infinite wave length and gives for the three substances the values 20.84 cc., 29.93 cc., and 18.55 cc., which show, as was expected, only relatively small differences from the constants $a = P_0$ derived from the measurements on the temperature-effect, perhaps excepting ethyl bromide.

TABLE X. *The Law of Temperature Effect for Monochlorobenzene.*

T	$P - P_0$	$(P - P_0)(T/300)$
193	76.6	49.3
203	73.1	49.5
213	70.1	49.8
223	67.1	49.9
233	64.1	49.8
243	61.1	49.5
253	59.4	50.1
263	57.6	50.4
273	55.6	50.6
283	53.6	50.5
293	51.6	50.4
303	49.1	49.6
313	47.9	50.0
323	46.9	50.5

[20] The corresponding values in Table VI are $\mu\,(CHCl_3) = 1.10 \times 10^{-18}$ and $\mu\,(C_6H\,Cl) = 1.52 \times 10^{-18}$.

In order to illustrate the temperature law by some figures I have taken for monochlorobenzene the refraction value $P_0 = 29.9$ cc., then taken the difference $P - P_0$ for different temperatures and calculated $(P - P_0)(T/300)$ (where the factor $1/300$ is again only introduced for convenience). This product should be constant, and is so indeed as is shown in Table X.

CHAPTER IV

THE CONSTITUTION OF SIMPLE POLAR MOLECULES

13. The Halogen-hydrides.

As shown experimentally by Zahn,[1] HCl, HBr and HI are polar, and nobody will have any doubt that the positive end of these molecules will be located near the H and the negative end near the halogen. But it would be interesting to have a more definite picture of the actual distribution of the charges. The simplest assumption for HCl, for instance, would be to assume a positive hydrogen ion combined with a negative chlorine ion, and to locate the centers of the charges in the mass centers, that is, in the nuclei of these ions. It can readily be shown, however, that this picture certainly does not hold.

It is well known that the absorption in the infra-red, due to the vibrations of the HCl in the direction of the line connecting the ions, consists of a series of absorption lines at both sides of the frequency corresponding to the natural frequency of the HCl vibration. The interpretation of this effect is that it is due to a superposition of the quantum rotation on the vibration, and the quantum theory gives for the frequency separation of two such lines the formula

$$\Delta \nu = \frac{h}{4\pi^2 A},$$

if we denote Planck's quantum (6.55×10^{-27} erg sec.) by h and the moment of inertia of the HCl molecule by A. So from the measured value of $\Delta \nu$ the moment of inertia A can be calculated, and from this the distance a of the two nuclei can be derived. In this way a is found to be 1.27×10^{-8} cm. If now the elementary charges $e = 4.77 \times 10^{-10}$ electrostatic units were located in these centers, the electric moment should have the value

$$\mu = ea = 6.06 \times 10^{-18} \text{ e.s.u.}$$

The measured value is

$$\mu = 1.03 \times 10^{-18} \text{ e.s.u.,}$$

nearly six times smaller. To account for this discrepancy it has to be borne in mind that, in the model we are discussing, the Cl-ion stands under the strain of the electric field of the H-ion; therefore a deformation of its electronic atmosphere is to be expected. As this deformation or polarization will have such a direction that its

[1] C. T. Zahn, *Phys. Rev.*, **24**, 400 (1924).

negative part is nearest to the positively charged H-ion, it is seen that the effect will be a diminution of the total electric moment. The large difference between the two values for μ mentioned above shows that the influence of such a polarization must be very appreciable, and it is indeed only by taking into account this effect that the characteristics of the simplest polar molecules can be interpreted.[2]

Let us consider the general case, where two atoms, 1 and 2, having charges $-e$ and $+e$ are located at a distance a apart and have polarizabilities α_1 and α_2. In reality this picture will give us only a second approximation, for at the small distances apart at which atoms in molecules are located an atom can only approximately be characterized by its charge and its polarizability. But introducing the polarizability is certainly the next step giving us, so to say, the second term in a series measuring the interaction, in which the first term is due to the interaction of the charges themselves. Let m_1 and m_2 denote the deformation moments set up in the atoms 1 and 2 respectively. The total intrinsic moment of the molecule may then be expressed by the equation

$$\mu = ea + m_1 + m_2.$$

If F_1 denotes the force acting on atom 1 due to atom 2, we have

$$m_1 = \alpha_1 F_1 = \alpha_1 \left(-\frac{e}{a^2} + \frac{2m_2}{a^3} \right),$$

and in like manner,

$$m_2 = \alpha_2 F_2 = \alpha_2 \left(-\frac{e}{a^2} + \frac{2m_1}{a^3} \right).$$

Solving these equations for m_1 and m_2, there results

$$m_1 = -\alpha_1 \frac{e}{a^2} \frac{1 + 2\dfrac{\alpha_2}{a^3}}{1 - 4\dfrac{\alpha_1}{a^3}\dfrac{\alpha_2}{a^3}},$$

$$m_2 = -\alpha_2 \frac{e}{a^2} \frac{1 + 2\dfrac{\alpha_1}{a^3}}{1 - 4\dfrac{\alpha_1}{a^3}\dfrac{\alpha_2}{a^3}}.$$

[2] The importance of the polarization effect for the interpretation of molecular forces was first mentioned by P. Debye [*Physik. Z.*, **21**, 178 (1920); **22**, 30 (1921)] in his theory of van der Waals' universal molecular attraction. References to the work of Wasastjerna, Fajans, Born and others, who discussed the magnitude and influence of the effect on the interatomic forces in the molecule, will be given elsewhere in this chapter. That the idea holds its place in modern quantum theory has recently been shown by A. Unsöld [*Z. Physik.*, **43**, 563 (1927)] for the interaction of a positive H-ion and a hydrogen-atom and by S. C. Wang, [*Physik. Z.*, **28**, 663 (1927)] for the interaction of two neutral H-atoms.

Substitution of these equations in the first equation gives

$$\mu = ea\left[1 - \frac{\dfrac{\alpha_1}{a^3} + \dfrac{\alpha_2}{a^3} + 4\dfrac{\alpha_1}{a^3}\dfrac{\alpha_2}{a^3}}{1 - 4\dfrac{\alpha_1}{a^3}\dfrac{\alpha_2}{a^3}}\right]. \qquad [33]$$

Let us now apply this result to the HCl molecule. The polarizability α_2 of the positive hydrogen ion is zero, and the polarizability α_1 of the negative chlorine ion may be called α. Then

$$\alpha_2 = 0, \qquad \alpha_1 = \alpha,$$

and [3]

$$\mu = ea\left[1 - \frac{\alpha}{a^3}\right]. \qquad [33']$$

In order to apply this relation, the polarizability α must be known. Now the atomic refraction P is related to α by the formula

$$P = \frac{4\pi}{3}N\alpha$$

and has been especially discussed by Fajans and Joos [4] and by Wasastjerna [5] also, in connection with the careful experiments of Heydweiller [6] on the refraction of salt solutions. The following list of atomic refractions P (in cc.) is due to Wasastjerna.

TABLE XI. *Atomic Refractions of Various Ions.*

O^{--}	4.06	F$^-$	2.20	Ne	1.01	Na$^+$	0.74	Mg^{++}	0.44
S^{--}	15.0	Cl$^-$	8.45	A	4.23	K$^+$	2.85	Ca^{++}	1.99
—		Br$^-$	11.84	K	6.42	Rb$^+$	4.41	Sr^{++}	3.22
—		I$^-$	18.47	Xe	10.56	Cs$^+$	7.36	Ba^{++}	5.24

If we adopt the value $P = 8.45$ given in the above table for the Cl-ion, the corresponding value of α will be

$$\alpha = 3.22 \times 10^{-24}.$$

[3] Compare also K. T. Compton's address in Kansas City, *Science*, **63**, 53, (1926).

[4] K. Fajans, *Naturwissenschaften*, **10**, 165 (1923); K. Fajans and G. Joos, *Z. Physik.*, **23**, 1 (1924).

[5] I. A. Wasastjerna, *Acta Soc. Scient. Fennicae*, **50**, 2 (1920); *Oeversike Finska Vet. Soc. Foerh.*, **63**, A, 4 (1920–21); *Comm. Phys. Math. Soc. Scient. Fennicae*, **1**, 37. The values of the atomic refraction given in the text are taken from a paper by the same author in *Comm. Phys. Math. Soc. Scient. Fennicae*, **1**, 38.

[6] A. Heydweiller, *Ann. Physik.*, **41**, 499 (1913); **48**, 681 (1915); **49**, 653 (1916); *Verhandl. deut. physik. Ges.*, **16**, 722 (1914).

With this value and the value formerly given for the distance a, equation [33'] would lead to

$$\mu = 6.06 \times 10^{-18} [1 - 1.63] = -3.8 \times 10^{-18}.$$

We first notice here that, according to the formula, the polarization effect would be able to over-compensate the moment of the ionic charges. Apart from the fact that such a behavior seems improbable and appears to be connected with an improper application of the theory to distances which are too small, the absolute value does not check with the experimental value $\mu = 1.03 \times 10^{-18}$.

Now Wasastjerna has also computed the apparent radii with which ions enter in crystals and gives for these radii the following table, in which the values are expressed in Angström units [7] (1 Angström = 10^{-8} cm.).

TABLE XII. *Atomic Radii.*

O⁻⁻	1.32	F⁻	1.33	Na⁺	1.01	Mg⁺⁺	0.75
S⁻⁻	1.69	Cl⁻	1.72	K⁺	1.30	Ca⁺⁺	1.02
—		Br⁻	1.92	Rb⁺	1.50	Sr⁺⁺	1.20
—		I⁻	2.19	Cs⁺	1.75	Ba⁺⁺	1.40

As the separation of the nuclei in HCl is only 1.27×10^{-8} cm. it appears that the H-ion of this molecule has to enter into the Cl-ion and this again suggests that formula [33'] has been extrapolated to distances which are much too small. Nevertheless, we may apply this formula to calculate the apparent polarizability $\alpha_{app.}$, which would give a positive value of μ equal to the observed moment. If this is done, we find

$$\alpha_{app.} = 1.70 \times 10^{-24},$$

and the corresponding apparent atomic refraction is

$$P_{app.} = 4.31 \text{ cc.}$$

It is a peculiar fact that this apparent atomic refraction is nearly equal to the atomic refraction of argon, the inert atom with the same number of electrons as the Cl-ion. This is still more peculiar if we calculate in the same manner the apparent atomic refraction of the Br-ion and find for this the value 6.27 cc., which is again according to Table XI nearly equal to the atomic refraction of the corresponding inert atom krypton. In this connection it is also interesting to notice that Unsöld (*loc. cit.*) has recently calculated with the help of wave mechanics that the polarizability of the hydro-

---

[7] More recent calculations of V. M. Goldschmidt, "Geochemische Verteilungsgesetze der Elemente," VII, Oslo, 1926, show small differences with Wasastjerna's values.

gen atom decreases if a hydrogen atom comes near enough to the nucleus of the atom. We will not go into further calculations, but will stop with the conclusion that in order to account for the relatively small moment actually measured it will be necessary to take into account the finite deformation of the halogen ion, under the influence of the field of the hydrogen ion. From the quantum theory in its most modern form it has been possible to account for the repulsive forces acting between atoms at small distances; we may therefore expect that before long it will be possible to calculate the properties of such simple molecules as are here considered.

14. A Linear Model for the H_2O Molecule.

We will now consider the structure of the water molecule in greater detail. In this discussion, however, we will not follow the original method of Heisenberg and Hund in which the repulsive forces are introduced as power functions of the distance. The static properties of the model can as well be treated if the atoms are taken as hard spheres. It is evident, however, that our model would not enable us to calculate the natural frequencies, which are also treated in the papers to which we refer.[8]

The possibility of the linear arrangement of atoms $(H-O-H)$, shown in Figure 17, will first be considered. A hard spherical shell

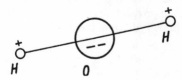

FIG. 17. Symmetrical linear H_2O model.

of radius a, serving as a picture for the O-atom, is supposed to act in such a way that when a hydrogen ion reaches this shell a repulsive force comes into action which would become infinitely large if the ion should enter the shell. If we should regard the coulomb forces due to the charges as the only forces existing, as was done by Kossel,[9] then both hydrogen ions would be located on this shell and no electric moment would exist, contrary to the experimental evidence (Table IV). Kossel's first approximation, therefore, although adequate to explain many properties in a beautiful way, is not sufficient if we wish to deal with the actual geometrical arrangement of the atoms in a molecule. We therefore take up the question as to the existence of a non-symmetrical arrangement, as shown in

[8] W. Heisenberg, Z. Physik., **26**, 196 (1924); F. Hund, Z. Physik., **31**, 81 (1925); **32**, 1 (1925).

[9] W. Kossel, Ann. Physik., **49**, 229 (1916).

Figure 18, introducing the polarizability of the atoms as the next approximation to reality.

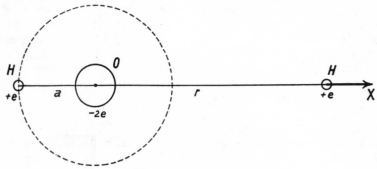

FIG. 18.   Unsymmetrical linear H_2O model.

Letting α denote the polarizability of the oxygen ion, the moment induced in this ion is

$$m = \alpha\left(\frac{e}{a^2} - \frac{e}{r^2}\right),$$

where a is the radius of the hard shell, indicated by the dotted circle, and r is the distance from the center of the shell to the second hydrogen ion.   The expression for the electric intensity at the location of the right-hand hydrogen ion then consists of three terms. The first

$$-2\frac{e}{r^2}$$

is due to the charge $-2e$ of the O-ion; the second

$$+\frac{e}{(r+a)^2}$$

is due to the charge of the left-hand H-ion; finally, the third is due to the moment m induced in the O-ion and has the value

$$\frac{2\alpha}{r^3}\left(\frac{e}{a^2} - \frac{e}{r^2}\right).$$

The actual force on the most distant hydrogen ion is

$$eX = \frac{e^2}{a^2}\left[-\frac{2}{x^2} + \frac{1}{(1+x)^2} + \frac{2\beta}{x^3}\left(1 - \frac{1}{x^2}\right)\right], \qquad [34]$$

where

$$\beta = \frac{\alpha}{a^3} \qquad \text{and} \qquad x = \frac{r}{a}. \qquad [34']$$

Let the terms of the right-hand side of this equation be denoted by

$$-\frac{2}{x^2} + \frac{1}{(1 + x)^2} = t_1, \Big\}$$
$$\frac{1}{x^3}\left(1 - \frac{1}{x^2}\right) = t_2; \Big\}$$

[34″]

then

$$eX = \frac{e^2}{a^2}[t_1 + 2\beta t_2].$$

[35]

We now proceed to determine the various equilibrium positions of the hydrogen ion upon which this force acts, also giving consideration to the question of the stability or instability of these positions. For this purpose the above equation is graphed, using β as a parameter, as shown by Figure 19. The curve I is a graph for the part

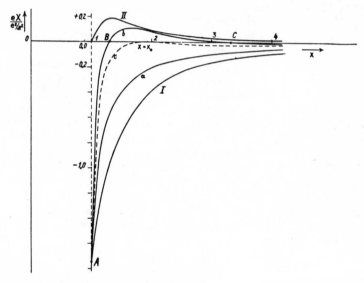

Fig. 19. Stability of the linear H_2O model.

t_1 and has negative ordinates for the whole interval between $x = 1$ and $x = \infty$. The curve II represents the part t_2; the ordinates are zero at the ends of the interval, are always positive, and reach a maximum value for $x = \sqrt{5/3}$. If now the polarizability α and therefore, according to [34′], β is small, then the sum $t_1 + 2\beta t_2$ will always be negative (Curve a). If β is large, then for a part of our interval the absolute value of $2\beta t_2$ will be larger than the absolute value of t_1 and we get a curve of type b, cutting the x-axis in two points. The transition of the two types will occur for a certain value $\beta = \beta_0$, which will have to be chosen in such a way that the curve $t_1 + 2\beta t_2$ just touches the x-axis at a point $x = x_0$ (Curve c).

From the above figure it follows that for $0 < \beta < \beta_0$ the symmetrical molecule is the only possible type, since in this case the hydrogen ion will be attracted for every value of x and cannot be in equilibrium until it is in contact with the hard shell. For values of β greater than β_0 there are three possible equilibrium positions, corresponding to A, B, and C. Only the two positions B and C correspond to an unsymmetrical model. Of these two, position B is clearly unstable, since if the hydrogen ion should be displaced slightly to the right of this position it would continue moving to the right, due to the (positive) repulsive force, while if displaced to the left it would be attracted and therefore continue moving to the left. From considerations exactly similar to these it may be shown that the position C is one of stable equilibrium. Heisenberg was therefore led to the conclusion that a linear non-symmetrical water molecule carrying a finite electric moment is possible if only the polarizability of the oxygen ion is large enough.

In the foregoing discussion, however, we only considered displacements in the direction of the line connecting the three atoms, which we will call radial displacements. It was shown by Hund that a molecule of this type is unstable if not only small radial but also small tangential displacements (*i.e.*, displacements normal to the connecting line) are considered. Before passing to this discussion let us determine the limiting values β_0 and x_0, which separate the non-symmetrical from the symmetrical forms. The significance of these critical values may be seen at once from Figure 19. If $\beta = \beta_0$ is chosen, such that the curve of the transition type c occurs, we will have at the point $x = x_0$ a zero ordinate and at the same time a first differential coefficient equal to zero. From equation [34] then there results

$$0 = \left[-\frac{2}{x_0{}^2} + \frac{2}{(1+x_0)^2} + \frac{2\beta_0}{x^3}\left(1 - \frac{1}{x_0{}^2}\right) \right],$$

$$0 = \frac{d}{dx_0}\left[-\frac{2}{x_0{}^2} + \frac{1}{(1+x_0)^2} + \frac{2\beta}{x_0{}^3}\left(1 - \frac{1}{x_0{}^2}\right) \right].$$

After performing the indicated differentiation in the second equation the value of x_0 which satisfies the two equations may be found by eliminating β_0. Substituting $x_0 = 1/y_0$, there results from our two equations

$$2\beta_0 = \frac{2 - \dfrac{1}{(1+y_0)^2}}{y_0(1-y_0)^2} = \frac{4 - \dfrac{2}{(1+y_0)^3}}{y_0(3 - 5y_0{}^2)}. \qquad [36]$$

The only real value of y_0 which satisfies this equation in the interval $0 \leqq y_0 \leqq 1$ (corresponding to $1 < x_0 < \infty$) is

$$y_0 = 0.54, \text{ corresponding to } x_0 = 1.85;$$

hence, using [36] again,

$$\beta_0 = 2.06.$$

A non-symmetrical water molecule is only possible, therefore, providing $\beta = \alpha/a^3$ is greater than 2.06 and $x = r/a$ is greater than 1.85.

We will now take $\beta > 2.06$ and show that the molecule cannot be in stable equilibrium if small tangential instead of radial displacements are considered. Such a displacement of the hydrogen ion is shown in Figure 20. In this figure h denotes a small tangential

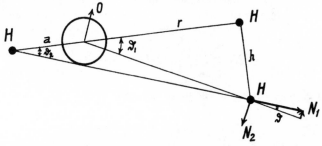

Fig. 20.   Instability for lateral displacements from the linear H_2O model.

displacement of the H-ion and N is used to denote the tangential force, taken as positive in the direction pointing towards the original position of the H-ion, so that the model is stable so long as N is positive.

Now let

$$N = N_1 + N_2,$$

where N_1 denotes the tangential force due to the repulsion of the other H-ion and N_2 the tangential force due to the electric moment of the oxygen ion. Clearly N then represents the total tangential force, since the attracting force due to the charge of the oxygen ion is entirely radial.

For the small displacement h we have, neglecting second order quantities,

$$N_1 = \frac{e}{(r + a)^2} \sin \vartheta = \frac{e}{(r + a)^2} \vartheta.$$

From the figure

$$\vartheta = \vartheta_1 - \vartheta_2 = \frac{h}{r} - \frac{h}{r + a}$$

and therefore

$$N_1 = \frac{e}{(r + a)^2}\left(\frac{h}{r} - \frac{h}{r + a}\right) = \frac{e}{a^2}\vartheta_1\frac{1}{(1 + x)^3}\,.$$

Again referring to Figure 20, it is seen that the moment set up in the oxygen ion, by the hydrogen ion which has been displaced, does not contribute to N_2. The force N_2 is due only to the tangential component of the moment induced by the fixed hydrogen ion and is given by the equation

$$N_2 = -\frac{\alpha e}{a^2}\vartheta_1\frac{1}{r^3} = -\frac{e}{a^2}\vartheta_1\frac{\beta}{x^3}\,.$$

Remembering that the induced moment is $\alpha(e/a^2)$, a simple calculation will show that the expression for N_2 is correct, the negative sign following from the direction of the lines of force of this moment. The total tangential component is

$$N = N_1 + N_2 = \frac{e}{a^2}\vartheta_1\left[\frac{1}{(1 + x)^3} - \frac{\beta}{x^3}\right],$$

so that N is negative and the model *unstable* if

$$\beta > \left(\frac{x}{1 + x}\right)^3\,.$$

Summing up, we first found it necessary that β should be larger than 2.06 in order for an unsymmetrical model to be possible. We now find that if β is larger than a certain other value given by $x^3/(1 + x)^3$ this model will be unstable for tangential displacements. The only values of x we have to consider range between $x = x_0 = 1.85$ and $x = \infty$. In this interval the expression $x^3/(1 + x)^3$ ranges from 0.27 to 1. In order that the unsymmetrical model could exist, β had to be larger than 2.06. Therefore β is certainly *always* larger than the expression $x^3/(1 + x)^3$ and the linear model can never be stable.

15. The Triangular Model for H_2O and the Pyramidal Model for NH_3.

Having shown that the linear non-symmetrical water molecule is unstable, we will now consider the possibility of a triangular molecule, where the hydrogen ions are located at the shell of radius a, which is concentric with the oxygen ion.[10] Such a molecule is

[10] In the case of this triangular model it is not necessary to consider non-symmetrical arrangements, since such arrangements would prevent an equilibrium condition from being attained.

pictured in Figure 21. The potential energy of this molecule is

$$u = -4\frac{e^2}{a} + \frac{e^2}{s} - \frac{\alpha}{2}\left(2\frac{e}{a^2}\cos\vartheta\right)^2. \qquad [37]$$

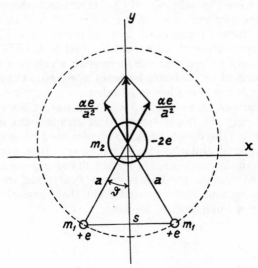

FIG. 21.   Actual stable triangular H_2O model.

The first two terms of this equation are the usual coulomb terms, while the third term is due to the polarization of the oxygen ion, and follows from the fact that the potential energy of a polarized atom in a field F is expressed by $-(\alpha/2)F^2$. From the figure

$$s = 2a\sin\vartheta$$

and the potential energy may be written as

$$u = -\frac{e^2}{a}\left[4 - \frac{1}{2\sin\vartheta} + 2\beta\cos^2\vartheta\right], \qquad [37']$$

where β is again used to denote α/a^3. In order to determine conditions of equilibrium the values of ϑ which will make the potential energy a minimum must be determined. Differentiating [37'] gives

$$\frac{\partial u}{\partial\vartheta} = -\frac{e^2}{2a}\cos\vartheta\left[\frac{1}{\sin^2\vartheta} - 8\beta\sin\vartheta\right];$$

in order for $\partial u/\partial\vartheta$ to reduce to zero it is necessary that either

$$\cos\vartheta = 0 \qquad [38]$$

or

$$\sin^3 \vartheta = \frac{1}{8\beta}, \qquad [38']$$

both of which are possibilities. If [38] is satisfied (thereby making $\partial u/\partial \vartheta = 0$, independent of β), we have $\vartheta = \pi/2$, and this gives the symmetrical linear arrangement first discussed. For [38'] to be satisfied for real values of ϑ we must have $8\beta > 1$, i.e., $\alpha/a^3 > 1/8$. From [38'] it is also seen that as β increases the angle must decrease, so that the form of the molecule becomes more acute the greater the polarizability of the O-ion has to be taken.

For the various values which β might assume, it is seen that for $0 < \beta < 1/8$ only the linear symmetrical arrangement is possible, while for $\beta > 1/8$ there seem to exist two possible arrangements, one linear symmetrical and the other triangular. However, we now show that, in the last case, only the triangular arrangement is stable.

First let us examine the linear symmetrical model for stability. If the hydrogen ions are displaced from their normal positions, changing ϑ by a small angle ϵ, we have

$$\vartheta = \frac{\pi}{2} + \epsilon$$

and to the third order in ϵ, according to [37'],

$$u = \frac{e^2}{a}\left[-\frac{7}{2} + \left(\frac{1}{4} - 2\beta\right)\epsilon^2 \right].$$

It follows from this equation that the effect of the small displacement ϵ will be to increase the potential energy if $\beta < 1/8$, and we therefore conclude that for $\beta < 1/8$ the only possible linear and symmetrical arrangement is stable. For values of $\beta > 1/8$, however, the sign of the term involving ϵ^2 is reversed and the arrangement will be unstable.

Now let us examine the triangular arrangement for stability. Letting ϑ_0 denote the value of ϑ satisfying the equilibrium condition [38'], we assume $\vartheta = \vartheta_0 + \eta$. In order to determine the effect of the small displacement η on the potential energy, we may develop u as given by [37'] in powers of η, finding for u the expression

$$u = u_0 + \frac{3}{2}\frac{e^2}{a}\beta^{1/3}(4\beta^{2/3} - 1)\eta^2,$$

where we have taken into account [38'] connecting ϑ_0 and β. The second term of this equation will be positive providing $(4\beta^{2/3} - 1) > 0$, which requires that $\beta > 1/8$. It follows that [38'] gives a condition of *stable* equilibrium, since for the triangular arrangement we have already found that we must have $\beta > 1/8$ for equilibrium.

From the values given in Tables XI and XII for α and a, we will expect α to be but slightly smaller than a^3. Therefore we may expect $\beta > 1/8$, and it follows that the linear symmetrical model would be unstable, and the molecule must therefore be of the triangular type having a permanent moment.

This conclusion is also in agreement with measurements on the absorption lines in the infra-red spectrum, the explanation of which requires the recognition of three distinct moments of inertia, in the case of the water molecule. By means of the absorption spectra Eucken [11] calculated these three moments of inertia and gave the following values:

$$2.25 \times 10^{-40}; \qquad 0.98 \times 10^{-40}; \qquad 3.2 \times 10^{-40}.$$

With the aid of these results we can determine the angle ϑ. For suppose the mass of the oxygen ion is m_2 and the hydrogen ions each have a mass m_1 as shown in Figure 21. Let the axes x, y, z be introduced, with the origin coinciding with the centroid of the molecule. [12] Let θ_1, θ_2, and θ_3 denote the moments of inertia with respect to the x-, y-, z-axes, respectively. Since three points define a plane, the z-coordinates of the three masses are zero and therefore the relation

$$\theta_1 + \theta_2 = \theta_3$$

will hold. It is satisfied by the values given by Eucken. Introducing

$$2m_1 + m_2 = m; \qquad \frac{m_1}{m} = \kappa_1; \qquad \frac{m_2}{m} = \kappa_2,$$

we have

$$\left. \begin{aligned}
\theta_1 &= ma^2 2\kappa_1\kappa_2 \cos^2 \vartheta, \\
\theta_2 &= ma^2 2\kappa_1 \sin^2 \vartheta, \\
\theta_3 &= ma^2 2\kappa_1(1 - 2\kappa_1 \cos^2 \vartheta).
\end{aligned} \right\} \qquad [39]$$

Since in our case $\kappa_1 = 1/18$ and $\kappa_2 = 16/18$, the first two equations of [39] will give

$$\tan^2 \vartheta = \frac{8}{9} \frac{\theta_2}{\theta_1}.$$

Referring to the data given by Eucken, it is evident that we could have either (a) $\theta_1 = 2.25 \times 10^{-40}$ and $\theta_2 = 0.98 \times 10^{-40}$ or (b) $\theta_1 = 0.98 \times 10^{-40}$ and $\theta_2 = 2.25 \times 10^{-40}$. Let us consider each possibility in turn. Supposition (a) will give $\vartheta = 32°$ and supposition (b) will give $\vartheta = 55°$. In order to determine which of these values of ϑ represents reality, let us calculate the electric moment of

[11] A. Eucken, Z. Elektrochem., 26, 377 (1920).
[12] For the direction of the x- and y-axis see Fig. 21; the z-axis may be taken perpendicular to the plane of the triangle.

the molecule for each case and compare the resulting values with the experimental value given by Jona.

Referring to Figure 21, let the electric moment be considered positive if it points in the direction from the O-ion to a point midway between the H-ions. The electric moment may then be written as

$$\mu = 2ea \cos \vartheta - \alpha \frac{2e}{a^2} \cos \vartheta,$$

where the first term of the right-hand member is the moment due directly to the charges carried by the ions and the second term is due to the polarizability of the oxygen ion.

Remembering that $\beta = \alpha/a^3$ and that the angle ϑ was connected with β by the equilibrium equation

$$\sin^3 \vartheta = \frac{1}{8\beta},$$

we may pass from the last written equation for μ to

$$\mu = 2ea \cos \vartheta \left[1 - \frac{1}{8} \frac{1}{\sin^3 \vartheta} \right]. \qquad [40]$$

For $\vartheta = 32°$ (Case a) this gives

$$\frac{\mu}{2ea} = 0.131,$$

while for $\vartheta = 55°$ (Case b)

$$\frac{\mu}{2ea} = 0.443.$$

Furthermore we can calculate the values of a in the two cases, using the given values of the moments of inertia. If we eliminate ϑ from the first two equations [39], the result is

$$ma^2 = \frac{\theta_1 + \kappa_2\theta_2}{2\kappa_1\kappa_2},$$

where the mass m of the H_2O molecule will be taken as $m = 29.5 \times 10^{-24}$ grams. We find in Case (a) the distance a to be 1.07×10^{-8} while for Case (b) it is 1.02×10^{-8}. These values of a may be substituted in the formula for $\mu/2ea$ and give the values $\mu = 1.34 \times 10^{-18}$ corresponding to Case (a) and $\mu = 4.32 \times 10^{-18}$ corresponding to Case (b).

From measurements on the variation of the dielectric constant of water vapor with temperature Jona found $\mu = 1.87 \times 10^{-18}$. Recalling that Jona's values are usually slightly larger than those obtained by other investigators, we conclude that $\mu = 1.34 \times 10^{-18}$ is much the more probable of the two calculated values of the moment. The equilibrium condition enables us to calculate β, and since we know a also, we can calculate the values of α or of the molar polarization $P = (4\pi/3)N\alpha$. All values are contained in the following table.

TABLE XIII. *Data for the Two Possible H_2O Models.*

Case (a)	Case (b)
$\vartheta = 32°$	$\vartheta = 55°$
$a = 1.07 \times 10^{-8}$	$a = 1.02 \times 10^{-8}$
$\beta = 0.848$	$\beta = 0.227$
$P = 2.64$	$P = 0.617$
$\mu = 1.34 \times 10^{-18}$	$\mu = 4.32 \times 10^{-18}$

Figure 22 gives pictures for the H_2O molecule in the two different

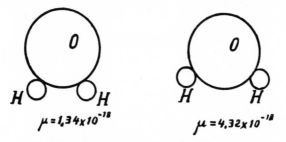

FIG. 22.   Two possible triangular H_2O models.

cases. The acute model, from what we have said, is the more probable.

The values given by Wasastjerna are 1.32×10^{-8} for the radius of the O-ion and 4.06 for the molar polarization (Tables XI and XII). Since these values are larger than the calculated value in Case (a), it appears very probable that the hydrogen atoms enter into the outer electron shell of the oxygen atom, corresponding to what we found for the halogen-hydrides. Similar triangular models are probable for the molecules H_2S, SO_2, $C_2H_5OC_2H_5$, etc.

The NH_3 molecule may be treated in exactly the same manner as we have treated the H_2O molecule, the result being a symmetrical pyramidal model as shown in Figure 23. The potential energy of this model is found to be

$$u = -\frac{9e^2}{a}\left[1 - \frac{1}{3\sqrt{3}}\frac{1}{\sin \vartheta} + \frac{\beta}{2}\cos^2 \vartheta\right], \qquad [41]$$

where ϑ denotes the angle between the vertical axis and a side a. The equilibrium condition, $\partial u/\partial\vartheta = 0$, is satisfied providing either

$$\cos\vartheta = 0$$

or

$$\sin^3\vartheta = \frac{1}{3\sqrt{3}}\frac{1}{\beta}.$$

The first condition corresponds to the case in which all four ions would lie in the same plane. In such a case there could be no electric

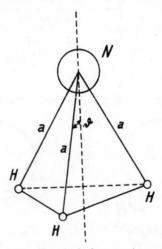

FIG. 23. Tetrahedral ammonia model.

moment, which is contrary to experimental evidence. The second pyramidal case requires that

$$\beta > \frac{1}{3\sqrt{3}}.$$

Proceeding in the same manner as in the case of the H_2O molecule, it may be shown that when this condition is satisfied the pyramidal model is stable, whereas the plane model is unstable. Since the NH_3 molecule is decidedly polar, we have to assume $\beta > (1/3\sqrt{3})$ and the pyramidal form to hold.

We will close these considerations with a somewhat more detailed discussion of the compensation effect due to the deformation. In the case of the H_2O molecule we have seen in equation [40] that

$$\frac{\mu}{2ea} = \cos\vartheta\left[1 - \frac{1}{8}\frac{1}{\sin^3\vartheta}\right].$$

The quantity $2ea$ represents the maximum moment the molecule could have, neglecting polarization of the oxygen ion.   The above equation therefore expresses the ratio of the true moment to this maximum moment as a function of the angle ϑ.   This result is shown graphically by Figure 24.

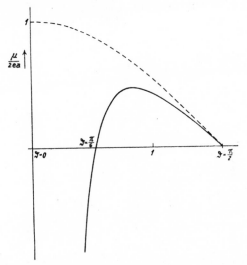

FIG. 24.   Effect of distortion on the moment of H_2O.

Referring to the figure, the dotted curve shows the manner in which the ratio of the true moment to the maximum moment would vary with the angle if there were no polarization effects, while the full curve shows the true variation of this ratio, taking account of polarization.   But according to [38'] the angle ϑ is connected with the polarizability of the O-ion in such a way that with increasing values of β the angle ϑ decreases from $\pi/2$ to zero, provided β is larger than the critical value.   Beginning with the point $\vartheta = \pi/2$ in the figure, then, it is seen that the moment first increases with increasing β, due to the fact that the distance between the center of the O-ion and the line connecting the two H-nuclei increases. But soon a compensation effect, due to the increasing polarization of the O-ion occurs, which is even able to compensate totally the moment due to the ionic charges for $\vartheta = 30°$ ($\beta = 1$), and to over-compensate this moment for larger values of β.   For $\vartheta = 32°$ (the experimental value of ϑ; see Table XIII) the effect of polarization is to greatly reduce the moment.

Quite similar curves may be plotted for molecules of the type of the NH_3 molecule, total compensation occurring in this case for an angle $\vartheta = 37° \, 40'$.

In all these calculations it should be borne in mind that, although the introduction of the polarizability leads to a second approximation, it is to be expected that differences between the arrangement in the picture and the real molecule will remain. However we do not expect that the conclusions about the general triangular or pyramidal form will be invalidated.

CHAPTER V

ANOMALOUS DISPERSION FOR RADIO FREQUENCIES

16. Generalization of the Boltzmann-Maxwell Distribution Function.

In Section 10 we referred to the fact that the polarization due to orientation will vanish for sufficiently high frequencies, thereby leaving only the distortion effect which is responsible for the refraction index measured for visible light. The question we will now take up is as to the particular frequency for which the transition of the statical to the optical polarization occurs. If we take polar molecules in the gaseous state, in which the interaction of the molecules may be neglected, we are merely dealing with the dispersion theory for a single molecule. Ultimately this is a question to be treated by the quantum theory and as such it is taken up in Chapter X. If we are dealing with liquids, however, the interaction is so strong that a treatment along very different lines, more closely related to classical statistics, seems preferable, and the impression prevails that quantum theory would not introduce essential changes in the principal results.

An anomalous dispersion in liquids for relatively long waves, *i.e.*, the decrease of the dielectric constant with increasing frequency, was first observed by Drude.[1] He found that this effect only existed for a certain kind of molecules in which, as he infers, special atomic groups like OH or NH_2 have to be existent. From our present point of view it is very probable that the characteristic property of the liquids with anomalous dispersion in the radio range is the polarity of their molecules, and that the effect represents the transition of the combined orientation and distortion to a pure distortion of the molecules.[2] The dividing line between these two effects may be said to occur at a frequency ν defined by the equation $\nu\tau = 1$, where τ is what we may appropriately call the time of relaxation of the liquid. More specifically τ is defined as the time required for the moments of the molecules to revert practically to a random distribution after removal of the impressed field.

The general question we will have to answer is how to find the distribution function of the moments if affected by a field variable with the time. For this purpose we cannot appeal to the familiar Maxwell-Boltzmann function, since this function only takes account

---

[1] P. Drude, in a number of publications to which references are given in his comprehensive article Z. *physik. Chem.*, **23**, 267 (1897).

[2] P. Debye, *Ber.*, **15**, 777 (1913); J. H. Tummers, Diss. Utrecht, 1914.

of the case of statistical equilibrium.   A sufficiently general mathematical basis, however, is provided by the theory of the Brownian movement.   It is with the help of this theory, following Einstein,[3] in general lines, that we will derive a partial differential equation defining the distribution function in the general case.   Here we will treat a field of force of one direction only, as this is sufficient for the dispersion problem.[4]   Moreover we will not treat saturation effects, since the intensities with which the dispersion is measured are always so small that no influence of higher powers than the first, of the field intensity, are of any importance.   For the statical case this would mean that, instead of using the Maxwell-Boltzmann expression

$$e^{-(u/kT)} = e^{\mu F/kT} \cos \vartheta$$

for the distribution function related to an electric moment μ making an angle ϑ with the field intensity F, we take only the first terms

$$1 + \frac{\mu F}{kT} \cos \vartheta$$

of the development.   To show that this approximation is sufficiently accurate we may substitute numerical values, for instance $\mu = 10^{-18}$, $F = 1$ e.s.u. $= 300$ volts/cm., $k = 1.37 \times 10^{-16}$, $T = 300$, which will give

$$\frac{\mu F}{kT} = 2.4 \times 10^{-5}.$$

Now let us consider the general case in which the impressed field is variable in time but constant in direction.   If we then suppose a spherical surface drawn in the liquid, and take the center of this sphere as the pole of a system of polar coordinates, it is obvious that the distribution function for the electric moments will depend upon the polar angle ϑ and upon the time.   The number of molecules which at a given time have their moments in the direction of a solid angle $d\Omega$ is $f d\Omega$.   This number will not remain constant, however, since the molecules are being continually reoriented, due to the varying field and due to the Brownian movement.

Now suppose that $f d\Omega$ is the number of molecules whose moments are in the solid angle $d\Omega$ at the beginning of an interval δt of observation, and let $t = 0$ denote the beginning of this interval.   We suppose that δt is large enough for all the molecules whose moments were in $d\Omega$ at $t = 0$ to have shifted outside this angle when $t = \delta t$.   We must furthermore suppose that δt is small enough so that during this interval the moments will not have had time to shift more than a few degrees.   Without the latter restriction we could not make

[3] A. Einstein, *Ann. Physik.*, **17**, 549 (1905); **19**, 371 (1906).
[4] For a more general formula compare P. Debye, "Handbuch der Radiologie," Vol. 5, p. 656.

certain mathematical simplifications which will lead to a relatively simple equation. It is evident that the second restriction prevents us from dealing with fields which are changing too rapidly, but it can be shown that for ordinary liquids the frequency for which the anomalous dispersion actually occurs is small enough not to interfere with this restriction. With these preliminary remarks we now proceed to develop the main argument.

The number of molecules whose moments have entered $d\Omega$ during the interval δt is given by the equation

$$\delta t \frac{\partial f}{\partial t} d\Omega = \Delta_1 + \Delta_2, \qquad [42]$$

where Δ_1 denotes the contribution due to rotations produced by the impressed field and Δ_2 denotes the contribution due to rotations produced by the Brownian movement. Let us first focus our attention on the term Δ_2. In order to discuss this term let us imagine a second solid angle $d\Omega'$, whose axis makes an angle θ with the axis of the solid angle $d\Omega$. Now suppose we have a certain probability function W such that $Wd\Omega$ denotes the probability that a molecule whose moment lies in $d\Omega'$ at the time $t = 0$ will have its moment in $d\Omega$ when $t = \delta t$. The total number of molecules whose moments have entered $d\Omega$ due to the Brownian movement in the interval δt is then given by

$$\Delta_2 = - fd\Omega + \int f' d\Omega' Wd\Omega,$$

where f' is the distribution function corresponding to the angle ϑ' of Fig. 25, and the integration is to be carried out over the surface of the sphere, of unit radius, while $d\Omega$ is fixed. The first term of this equation accounts for all the molecules whose moments pass out of $d\Omega$ during the interval δt and which were there at $t = 0$, and the second term accounts for all the molecules having moments outside of $d\Omega$ when $t = 0$ which have taken up positions in $d\Omega$ at the completion of the given interval. It is clear that the probability function W will be a function of θ alone, while the space variation of f will depend upon ϑ alone. Since $d\Omega$ is constant with respect to the integration, we may write

$$\Delta_2 = d\Omega \{ \int f' Wd\Omega' - f \}. \qquad [43]$$

If the function f' is expanded about its value at $d\Omega$, we obtain

$$f' = f + (\vartheta' - \vartheta) \frac{\partial f}{\partial \vartheta} + \frac{(\vartheta' - \vartheta)^2}{2} \frac{\partial^2 f}{\partial \vartheta^2} + \cdots.$$

Now, according to our second restriction on δt the probability function W must approach zero very rapidly when θ exceeds a few degrees. In order to evaluate the integral in the equation for Δ_2 we need therefore consider only small values of θ and therefore of $(\vartheta' - \vartheta)$, so that the fourth and higher order terms in the expansion

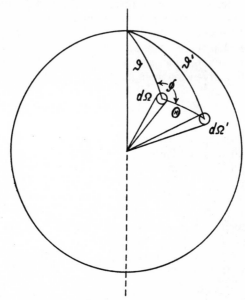

FIG. 25.   Diagram for Brownian movement of dipoles.

for f' may be neglected.   Letting $\vartheta' - \vartheta = \epsilon$, we thus obtain

$$\int f' W d\Omega' = f \int W d\Omega' + \frac{\partial f}{\partial \vartheta} \int \epsilon W d\Omega' + \frac{1}{2} \frac{\partial^2 f}{\partial \vartheta^2} \int \epsilon^2 W d\Omega'.$$

The first integral of the right-hand member is clearly equal to unity. It is also evident that the second integral of the right-hand member represents the mean value $\bar{\epsilon}$ of ϵ corresponding to the time δt, and the third integral in a similar way represents the mean square value $\bar{\epsilon^2}$ of ϵ.   We now turn to the evaluation of these integrals. From spherical trigonometry

$$\cos \vartheta' = \cos \vartheta \cos \theta + \sin \vartheta \sin \theta \cos \phi,$$

and since we need consider only small values of θ this may be written as

$$\cos \vartheta' = \cos \vartheta + \theta \sin \vartheta \cos \phi - \frac{\theta^2}{2} \cos \vartheta + \cdots.$$

But since $\vartheta' = \vartheta + \epsilon$ and ϵ must be small, we also have

$$\cos \vartheta' = \cos \vartheta - \epsilon \sin \vartheta - \frac{\epsilon^2}{2} \cos \vartheta + \cdots.$$

Now let us imagine ϵ to be expanded in powers of θ giving

$$\epsilon = \alpha\theta + \beta\theta^2 + \cdots,$$

where the coefficients involve functions of ϑ and ϕ implicitly. In order to arrive at the explicit form of the coefficients this expansion may be substituted in the last written expansion for cos ϑ' and then by comparing the two expansions for cos ϑ' it is found that

$$\epsilon = -\theta \cos \phi + \frac{\theta^2}{2} \frac{\cos \vartheta}{\sin \vartheta} \sin^2 \phi + \cdots.$$

Averaging this expression for ϵ over all directions gives

$$\bar{\epsilon} = \int \epsilon W d\Omega' = \int_{\theta=0}^{\pi} \int_{\phi=0}^{2\pi} \epsilon W \sin \theta d\theta d\phi$$

$$= \int_0^{\pi} \int_0^{2\pi} \frac{\theta^2}{2} W \frac{\cos \vartheta}{\sin \vartheta} \sin^2 \phi \sin \theta d\theta d\phi = \frac{\overline{\theta^2}}{4} \frac{\cos \vartheta}{\sin \vartheta},$$

where

$$\overline{\theta^2} = \int_0^{\pi} \int_0^{2\pi} \theta^2 W \sin \theta d\theta d\phi.$$

In a similar manner $\overline{\epsilon^2}$ may be evaluated, giving

$$\overline{\epsilon^2} = \int \epsilon^2 W d\Omega' = \frac{\overline{\theta^2}}{2},$$

and finally

$$\int f' W d\Omega' = f + \frac{\partial f}{\partial \vartheta} \frac{\cos \vartheta}{\sin \vartheta} \frac{\overline{\theta^2}}{4} + \frac{\overline{\theta^2}}{4} \frac{\partial^2 f}{\partial \vartheta^2},$$

giving for Δ_2, according to [43], the expression

$$\Delta_2 = d\Omega \frac{\overline{\theta^2}}{4} \left[\frac{\cos \vartheta}{\sin \vartheta} \frac{\partial f}{\partial \vartheta} + \frac{\partial^2 f}{\partial \vartheta^2} \right]. \qquad [44]$$

From this equation we see that if the moments have a random distribution, i.e., if f is independent of ϑ, the Brownian movement can have no effect on the distribution function. In the case of an impressed electric field, however, the distribution function will not be uniform, and hence will be affected by the Brownian movement as shown by the above equation.

We have yet to determine Δ_1, i.e., the number of molecules whose moments have entered $d\Omega$ in the interval δt due to the action of the impressed field. The torque on a given molecule tending to turn it in the direction of the field is

$$M = -\mu F \sin \vartheta,$$

where the negative sign takes account of the fact that the torque acts opposite to the direction of increasing ϑ. Under the influence of a constant torque the molecule would be rotated with an angular velocity proportional to the torque, or in other words a torque due to an inner frictional force resulting from molecular impacts, and proportional to the angular velocity, would just balance the constant impressed torque. We express this by the equation

$$M = \zeta \frac{d\vartheta}{dt},$$

where ζ is a constant measuring the inner friction. If we apply this equation to our case, in which the torque is not constant, we imply that the acceleration effect is negligibly small, as it is for instance in the analogous case of ions moving in a liquid.

In an interval δt the molecule will then turn through the angle

$$\delta\vartheta = \delta t \frac{M}{\zeta}.$$

Now let us determine the number of molecules, in the interval of time δt, whose moments enter a solid angle consisting of a strip extending between ϑ and $\vartheta + d\vartheta$ around the sphere. The number of molecules whose moments pass through the circle $\vartheta = \vartheta$ in the interval δt is

$$2\pi f \sin \vartheta \delta\vartheta = 2\pi f \frac{M}{\zeta} \delta t \sin \vartheta$$

and they can be considered as entering the strip. The number of molecules whose moments pass through the circle $\vartheta + d\vartheta$ in the same interval of time is

$$2\pi f \frac{M}{\zeta} \delta t \sin \vartheta + \frac{\partial}{\partial \vartheta} \left(2\pi f \frac{M}{\zeta} \delta t \sin \vartheta \right) d\vartheta.$$

Taking the first expression with the positive sign, the second with the negative sign, and adding them, we will find the net change during δt of the number of moments pointing in the directions contained within the strip. As we called this number Δ_1, we have

$$\Delta_1 = - \frac{\partial}{\partial \vartheta} \left(2\pi f \frac{M}{\zeta} \delta t \sin \vartheta \right) d\vartheta. \qquad [45]$$

Substituting [44] and [45] in [42] and remembering that

$$d\Omega = 2\pi \sin \vartheta d\vartheta,$$

we obtain the equation

$$\frac{\partial f}{\partial t} = \frac{1}{\sin \vartheta} \frac{\partial}{\partial \vartheta} \left[\sin \vartheta \left\{ \frac{\overline{\theta^2}}{4\delta t} \frac{\partial f}{\partial \vartheta} - \frac{M}{\zeta} f \right\} \right]. \qquad [46]$$

The constant $\overline{\theta^2}/\delta t$, which is characteristic for this equation, is closely related to the well-known constant $\overline{x^2}/\delta t$ in the ordinary Brownian movement, in which particles travel over irregular linear distances x. In fact, its value can be found in the same way as was done by Einstein for the last-named constant.

Equation [46] has to express the distribution of the moments also in the special case where we are dealing with a constant field F, which requires that the Maxwell-Boltzmann expression

$$f = A e^{-(u/kT)} = A e^{(\mu F/kT)\cos \vartheta}$$

be a solution of the differential equation if

$$\frac{\partial f}{\partial t} = 0.$$

Since

$$M = -\mu F \sin \vartheta = -\frac{\partial u}{\partial \vartheta},$$

it is readily seen that this is the case, provided

$$\frac{\overline{\theta^2}}{4\delta t} = \frac{kT}{\zeta}. \qquad [47]$$

This equation expresses the general relation which exists between the magnitude of the Brownian "Schwankung" of the angle and the temperature and friction constant of the molecules. If we substitute in equation [46] the value of $\overline{\theta^2}/4\delta t$ given in [47], the final differential equation to determine the distribution function f as a function of t and ϑ is found to be

$$\zeta \frac{\partial f}{\partial t} = \frac{1}{\sin \vartheta} \frac{\partial}{\partial \vartheta} \left[\sin \vartheta \left(kT \frac{\partial f}{\partial \vartheta} - Mf \right) \right]. \qquad [48]$$

17. Relaxation Time of Polar Liquids.

Now returning to the original question as to the time required for the moments to revert to a random distribution after the removal of the impressed field, let us seek a solution of equation [48] for values of $t > 0$ subject to the conditions

$$F = F_0 \quad \text{for} \quad t < 0,$$
$$F = 0 \quad \text{for} \quad t > 0.$$

Since we require the solution only for $t > 0$ the torque may be put equal to zero and we have

$$\zeta \frac{\partial f}{\partial t} = \frac{kT}{\sin \vartheta} \frac{\partial}{\partial \vartheta} \left(\sin \vartheta \frac{\partial f}{\partial \vartheta} \right).$$

As a solution of this equation let us try

$$f = A\left[1 + \frac{\mu F_0}{kT}\, \varphi(t)\, \cos \vartheta \right],$$

where $\varphi(t)$ has still to be determined. Substitution of this function in the differential equation gives us the conditional equation

$$\frac{d\varphi}{dt} = -\frac{2kT}{\zeta}\, \varphi.$$

Hence φ has to be defined by the equation

$$\varphi(t) = e^{-(2kT/\zeta)t},$$

and it is clear that

$$f = A\left[1 + \frac{\mu F_0}{kT}\, e^{-(2kT/\zeta)t} \cos \vartheta \right] \qquad [49]$$

will satisfy the conditions of our problem; for when $t = 0$ this reduces to our approximation of the Maxwell-Boltzmann function. For $t = \infty$ it reduces to a constant and no direction is given a preference. The variable part of the distribution function will be reduced to $1/e$ of its initial value after a time of $\zeta/2kT$ seconds has elapsed. We therefore define the relaxation time by the equation

$$\tau = \zeta/2kT \qquad [50]$$

and write

$$f = A\left[1 + \frac{\mu F_0}{kT}\, e^{-(t/\tau)} \cos \vartheta \right]. \qquad [51]$$

We are now of course also in a position to calculate the mean moment and the molar polarization at any time t. The mean moment due to orientation alone is given by

$$\overline{m} = \frac{\int f d\Omega \mu \cos \vartheta}{\int f d\Omega}.$$

Using the Maxwell-Boltzmann distribution law for the stationary case, we evaluated this expression and found

$$\overline{m} = \frac{\mu^2}{3kT}\, F_0.$$

Hence in the present case, using the generalized distribution law [51], we will find by a similar procedure

$$\overline{m} = \frac{\mu^2}{3kT}\, F_0 e^{-(t/\tau)},$$

which follows at once since the function $\varphi(t) = e^{-(t/\tau)}$ is constant with respect to the integrations which were carried out to determine m in the simpler case. In the foregoing part the relaxation time τ can be considered as the unknown parameter and the answer to the question if our discussion about relaxation has anything to do with Drude's anomalous dispersion can only be given in considering the order of magnitude τ can have in our picture. Now Stokes calculated that when a sphere of radius a rotates in a liquid of inner friction constant η the frictional torque is $8\pi\eta a^3$ times the angular velocity of the sphere. For such a sphere therefore

$$\zeta = 8\pi\eta a^3. \qquad [52]$$

Suppose that for a we substitute a length of the order of magnitude of molecular dimensions and for η the inner friction constant of the liquid, as it is commonly defined. I think we then have a right to expect that the calculated value of ζ will be approximately correct even for the rotation of as small a particle as a molecule. The corresponding calculation for the mobility of ions or the rate of diffusion of molecules dissolved in liquids, in which the frictional force is related to a translational motion, is evaluated as $6\pi\eta a$ times the velocity (again according to another formula due to Stokes) and is known to give good results.

In the case of water at ordinary temperature $\eta = 0.01$; if we assume $a = 2 \times 10^{-8}$ we will find $\zeta = 2 \times 10^{-24}$ and according to equation [50] the relaxation time $\tau = 0.25 \times 10^{-10}$ sec. This time corresponds to a wave length of the order of magnitude 1 cm. and, as ζ changes very rapidly with a, we will expect that for different liquids a considerable range of wave lengths corresponding to high radio frequencies will be the characteristic region in which an anomalous dispersion resulting from orientation may be expected.

Although this calculation is of importance in as much as it gives the conviction that we are on the right track for the explanation of Drude's anomalous dispersion, it is by no means essential for the *formal* description of this effect. We can of course introduce the relaxation time τ as a parameter and derive this parameter from the experimental results. As an example we will treat briefly the case of a condenser containing a polar liquid which is short circuited at a given moment $t = 0$ by a resistance W. This example will also give a more complete statement in the actual case in which it is not possible to make an instantaneous change from $F = F$ to $F = 0$.

The molecule will be considered as having a polarizability α_0 due to distortion and a polarizability $\alpha_1 = (\mu^2/3kT)$ due to orientation. Moreover, the validity of Mosotti's assumption will be accepted. If then for the distribution function at any time we make the assumption

$$f = A \left[1 + \frac{\mu}{kT} X(t) \cos \vartheta \right]$$

and calculate the torque M by the equation

$$M = - \mu F \sin \vartheta,$$

it is seen by substitution in the fundamental equation [48], and remembering the definition of the relaxation time τ, that

$$\tau \frac{dX}{dt} + X = F. \qquad [53]$$

The supposition is made that F and X are of the same order of magnitude and, as we are not considering saturation effects, higher powers of these quantities than the first are neglected.

If the condenser consists of two plates of surface σ each and if the dielectric displacement is D, the total charge on one plate will be $(\sigma/4\pi)D$. The current is $- (\sigma/4\pi)(dD/dt)$; the electromotive force is the potential difference of the condenser plates and therefore is equal to El, if l is the distance between the plates and E the electric intensity. Now applying Ohm's law, we arrive at the equation

$$E + CW \frac{dD}{dt} = 0, \qquad [54]$$

denoting the quotient $\sigma/4\pi l$ by C, because it is the capacity of the empty condenser. In the two equations [53] and [54] four unknown quantities E, D, F, and X are introduced. We obtain two more equations in the general relations

$$D = E + 4\pi I, \qquad [55]$$

$$F = E + \frac{4\pi}{3} I, \qquad [56]$$

but in this way we introduce a fifth unknown quantity, the intensity of polarization I. The necessary fifth and last equation

$$I = n\alpha_0 F + n\alpha_1 X \qquad [57]$$

expresses how the polarization can be calculated introducing the number n of molecules per cc. and the molecular constants α_0 and $\alpha_1 = \mu^2/3kT$. The first part of the right-hand side in [57] is due to the moment $\alpha_0 F$ set up by distortion; the second part assumes the average moment (a space average being meant of course) due to orientation to be equal $(\mu^2/3kT)X$ at every instant. This is seen to hold if we calculate this average moment with the help of the formula for the distribution-function with which we started.

From a practical point of view the two quantities in which we are mainly interested are E and D, since these are connected with the potential difference Φ between the plates and the charge Q on one plate by the equations

$$\Phi = El \quad \text{and} \quad Q = \frac{\sigma}{4\pi} D.$$

Eliminating, therefore, I, F and X between the equations [53] to [57], we obtain

$$CW \frac{dD}{dt} + E = 0,$$

$$(1 - p_0)\tau \frac{dD}{dt} + (1 - p_0 - p_1)D = (1 + 2p_0)\tau \frac{dE}{dt} \left.\vphantom{\begin{matrix}1\\1\\1\end{matrix}}\right\} \quad [58]$$
$$+ (1 + 2p_0 + 2p_1)E,$$

where

$$p_0 = \frac{4\pi}{3} n\alpha_0 \quad \text{and} \quad p_1 = \frac{4\pi}{3} n\alpha_1. \quad [58']$$

The solution is found by the usual method in substituting

$$D = D^* e^{-(t/\theta)} \quad \text{and} \quad E = E^* e^{-(t/\theta)},$$

where D^* and E^* are constants and the time constant θ is one of the roots of the quadratic equation

$$\frac{CW}{\theta}\left[(1 + 2p_0 + 2p_1) - (1 + 2p_0)\frac{\tau}{\theta} \right]$$
$$-\left[(1 - p_0 - p_1) - (1 - p_0)\frac{\tau}{\theta} \right] = 0. \quad [59]$$

If no relaxation existed ($\tau = 0$), the time constant θ would be

$$\theta = \frac{1 + 2(p_0 + p_1)}{1 - (p_0 + p_1)} CW.$$

This is the well-known value for an ordinary condenser, for the constant multiplying CW is the ordinary dielectric constant ϵ according to Mosotti's rule, i.e.,

$$\epsilon = \frac{1 + 2(p_0 + p_1)}{1 - (p_0 + p_1)}.$$

In the general case, let us call the two roots θ_1 and θ_2 and the corresponding constants for the dielectric displacement D_1^* and D_2^*. We then have

$$D = D_1^* e^{-(t/\theta_1)} + D_2^* e^{-(t/\theta_2)} \quad [60]$$

and according to the first equation of [58]

$$E = \frac{CW}{\theta_1} D_1^* e^{-(t/\theta_1)} + \frac{CW}{\theta_2} D_2^* e^{-(t/\theta_2)}.$$

The other three quantities, I, F and X, can likewise be expressed with the help of D_1^* and D_2^*, using the three remaining equations. So, for instance, we will find

$$3p_1X = \left[(1 - p_0) - \frac{CW}{\theta_1} (1 + 2p_0) \right] D_1^* e^{-(t/\theta_1)}$$
$$+ \left[(1 - p_0) - \frac{CW}{\theta_2} (1 + 2p_0) \right] D_2^* e^{-(t/\theta_2)}. \qquad [60']$$

Now we have two conditions at the beginning $t = 0$ of the experiments. First we know the total charge on one plate of the condenser, or, in other words, we know the initial dielectric displacement, which we will call D_0. Secondly, we know that for $t = 0$ the distribution of the moments is given by Boltzmann's function. Calling F_0 the initial internal force, we know, therefore, that for $t = 0$ we have the condition $X(0) = F_0$. But in the statical case F_0 is found with the help of Mosotti's assumption to be equal to $[(\epsilon+2)/3\epsilon]D_0$ in a medium with the dielectric constant ϵ. Our second condition therefore has (for $t = 0$) the form

$$X(0) = \left[1 + 2 \frac{1 - (p_0 + p_1)}{1 + 2(p_0 + p_1)} \right] \frac{D_0}{3} = \frac{D_0}{1 + 2(p_0 + p_1)}.$$

Using both initial conditions, the two constants D_1^* and D_2^* can be expressed in terms of the initial displacement D_0. The final result for D is

$$\left(\frac{CW}{\theta_1} - \frac{CW}{\theta_2} \right) \frac{D}{D_0} = \left(\frac{CW}{\theta_1} e^{-(t/\theta_2)} - \frac{CW}{\theta_2} e^{-(t/\theta_1)} \right)$$
$$- \frac{1}{\epsilon} \left(e^{-(t/\theta_2)} - e^{-(t/\theta_1)} \right), \qquad [61]$$

showing that in general the time function is a superposition of two exponentials. A special case of some interest is obtained if the resistance W is taken so small that the usual time of discharge would be small compared with the relaxation time of the dielectric. From [59] it is found in the limit for $W = 0$ that

$$\frac{1}{\theta_1} = \frac{1 - p_0}{1 + 2p_0} \frac{1}{CW}, \qquad \frac{1}{\theta_2} = \frac{1 - p_0 - p_1}{1 - p_0} \frac{1}{\tau};$$

substituting these values in [61] yields

$$\frac{D}{D_0} = \frac{\epsilon_0}{\epsilon} e^{-(t/\epsilon_0 CW)} + \left(1 - \frac{\epsilon_0}{\epsilon} \right) e^{-(1-p_0-p_1)/(1-p_0)(\tau/t)}, \qquad [61']$$

where we have used the notation

$$\frac{1 + 2p_0}{1 - p_0} = \epsilon_0,$$

since this would be the dielectric constant if the molecules were non-polar ($\mu = 0$). Equation [61'] shows how a first part of the dielectric displacement ($\epsilon_0/\epsilon)D_0$, and therefore of the charge too, vanishes in a time comparable with $\epsilon_0 CW$, which is supposed to be a very short time. It is the time of discharge of a condenser filled with a fictitious substance whose dielectric constant would be determined by the distortion alone. The remaining part $[1 - (\epsilon_0/\epsilon)]D_0$ vanishes in a time comparable with $[(1-p_0)/(1-p_0-p_1)]\tau$, which can be several times the characteristic relaxation time τ if $p_0 + p_1$ is not very different from 1. This is to be expected for substances with a high dielectric constant, according to the formula

$$\epsilon = \frac{1 + 2(p_0 + p_1)}{1 - (p_0 + p_1)},$$

which will give large values of ϵ if the denominator does not differ greatly from zero.

18. Polar Liquids under the Influence of High Frequencies.

Practically much more important than the case treated in the foregoing Section 17 are the dielectric properties in a periodic field. Let the number of vibrations in 2π seconds be ω; the internal force may then be expressed by the real part of

$$F = F_0 e^{i\omega t},$$

so that the torque on a molecule is given by

$$M = -\mu F_0 e^{i\omega t} \sin \vartheta.$$

As in the previous case the distribution function must be a solution of [48], which we can write in the form

$$2\tau \frac{\partial f}{\partial t} = \frac{1}{\sin \vartheta} \frac{\partial}{\partial \vartheta} \left[\sin \vartheta \left(\frac{\partial f}{\partial \vartheta} - \frac{fM}{kT} \right) \right].$$

Let us try as a solution

$$f = A \left[1 + B \frac{\mu F_0}{kT} e^{i\omega t} \cos \vartheta \right],$$

where B is a constant as yet arbitrary. The substitution of this expression in [48] shows that the differential equation is satisfied, providing we choose B complex according to the equation [5]

$$B = \frac{1}{1 + i\omega\tau}.$$

We have then

$$f = A\left[1 + \frac{1}{1 + i\omega\tau}\frac{\mu F}{kT}\cos\vartheta\right]. \qquad [62]$$

For $\omega = 0$ we have the usual Maxwell-Boltzmann function, while for very large values of $\omega\tau$ the function becomes constant. The transition from one case to the other occurs for frequencies which will make $\omega\tau$ of order of magnitude unity. The mean moment of the molecules is also complex and is given by the equation

$$\overline{m} = \frac{\mu^2}{3kT}\frac{F}{1 + i\omega\tau} = \frac{\mu^2}{3kT}\frac{F_0 e^{i\omega t}}{1 + i\omega\tau}. \qquad [63]$$

The meaning of the complex moment is of course that there is a difference in phase between the moment and the internal force. If the phase angle is φ, the above equation may be written in the form

$$\overline{m} = \frac{\mu^2}{3kT}\frac{F_0}{\sqrt{1 + \omega^2\tau^2}}e^{i(\omega t - \varphi)},$$

where

$$\tan\varphi = \omega\tau.$$

Now it is well known that a difference in phase between field intensity and polarization is always accompanied by energy absorption. As a result of the existence of a finite relaxation time, we will therefore not only encounter dispersion but also absorption intimately connected with it.[6] We are going to consider these phenomena in some detail, assuming Mosotti's hypothesis to hold.

The molar polarization P in this case is expressed by

$$\frac{\epsilon - 1}{\epsilon + 2}\frac{M}{\rho} = P(\omega) = \frac{4\pi N}{3}\left[\alpha_0 + \frac{\mu^2}{3kT}\frac{1}{1 + i\omega\tau}\right], \qquad [64]$$

which is complex and a function of the frequency. Solving this

---

[5] Quantities of higher than the first order in F are again neglected.

[6] As another consequence of the existence of such a difference in phase it is known that in a rotating electric field of constant intensity a dielectric will begin to rotate. The reason why the phase difference exists does not matter at all; any dielectric showing conductivity or dielectric losses will exhibit the effect. [Compare A. Winkelmann, "Handbuch der Physik," IV, 1, p. 161, and G. Breit, Z. Physik, 11, 129 (1922).] M. Born, Z. Physik, 1, 221 (1920), starting from another point of view, calculated the torque on a polar liquid, whose absorption is due to the relaxation effect mentioned in the text. (Compare also P. Debye, "Handbuch der Radiologie," V, p. 652.) Successful experiments were carried out by P. Lertes, Z. Physik, 4, 56 (1921).

equation for ϵ, we find

$$\epsilon = \frac{1 + 2\dfrac{\rho}{M}P(\omega)}{1 - \dfrac{\rho}{M}P(\omega)} . \qquad [64']$$

Instead of characterizing the liquid by the two theoretical constants α_0 and $\mu^2/3kT$ it is advisable to use the two dielectric constants ϵ_0 and ϵ_1 defined by

$$\left.\begin{array}{l} \dfrac{\epsilon_0 - 1}{\epsilon_0 + 2}\dfrac{M}{\rho} = \dfrac{4\pi}{3}N\alpha_0, \\[3mm] \dfrac{\epsilon_1 - 1}{\epsilon_1 + 2}\dfrac{M}{\rho} = \dfrac{4\pi}{3}N\left(\alpha_0 + \dfrac{\mu^2}{3kT}\right). \end{array}\right\} \qquad [65]$$

According to [64] the dielectric constant ϵ_0 will then denote the value of ϵ for high frequencies, the optical dielectric constant, as we will call it, and ϵ_1 will be the statical dielectric constant, observed for $\omega = 0$. With these definitions the molar polarization takes the form

$$P(\omega) = \frac{M}{\rho}\left[\frac{\epsilon_0 - 1}{\epsilon_0 + 2} + \frac{1}{1 + i\omega\tau}\left(\frac{\epsilon_1 - 1}{\epsilon_1 + 2} - \frac{\epsilon_0 - 1}{\epsilon_0 + 2}\right)\right]$$

and we obtain for the dielectric constant as a function of ω the expression

$$\epsilon = \frac{\dfrac{\epsilon_1}{\epsilon_1 + 2} + i\omega\tau\dfrac{\epsilon_0}{\epsilon_0 + 2}}{\dfrac{1}{\epsilon_1 + 2} + i\omega\tau\dfrac{1}{\epsilon_0 + 2}} . \qquad [66]$$

According to the formal theory of propagation of light ϵ is equal to the square of the generalized refraction index, but as ϵ is here an imaginary quantity, the generalized refraction index will also have an imaginary part. In the usual way we therefore put

$$\epsilon = r^2(1 - i\kappa)^2 \qquad [66']$$

such that r and κ are both real quantities, r being the ordinary refraction index and κ the absorption index.

The meaning of the two constituents of the generalized refractive index is seen, if it is remembered that the field intensity of a plane wave travelling in the s-direction is proportional to the expression

$$e^{i\omega\left[t - \frac{r(1 - i\kappa)}{c}s\right]} = e^{-\omega\kappa\frac{r}{c}s}e^{i\omega\left[t - \frac{r}{c}s\right]},$$

if we denote by c the velocity of light in vacuum. If the wave-length in vacuum is λ_0, the wave-length in the medium is $\lambda = \lambda_0/r$ and the amplitude is multiplied by $e^{-2\pi\kappa}$ after the wave has travelled over a distance of one wave-length λ.

In order to discuss the refraction index r and the absorption index κ as functions of the frequency, we introduce the variable

$$x = \frac{\epsilon_1 + 2}{\epsilon_0 + 2} \omega\tau. \qquad [67]$$

It can then be shown that [66] is equivalent to the two equations

$$\left. \begin{aligned} r^2 &= \frac{1}{2}\left[\sqrt{\frac{\epsilon_1^2 + \epsilon_0^2 x^2}{1 + x^2}} + \frac{\epsilon_1 + \epsilon_0 x^2}{1 + x^2} \right], \\ r^2\kappa^2 &= \frac{1}{2}\left[\sqrt{\frac{\epsilon_1^2 + \epsilon_0^2 x^2}{1 + x^2}} - \frac{\epsilon_1 + \epsilon_0 x^2}{1 + x^2} \right], \end{aligned} \right\} \qquad [68]$$

giving values for r and for $r\kappa$ separately.

Calling $\epsilon_0/\epsilon_1 = p$, equation [66] can be written in the form

$$\frac{\epsilon}{\epsilon_1} = \frac{1 + ipx}{1 + ix}.$$

If now two angles φ and ψ are introduced by the equations $\tan \varphi = x$ and $\tan \psi = px$, it can be shown that

$$\frac{r^2}{\epsilon_1} = \frac{\cos \varphi}{\cos \psi} \cos^2\left(\frac{\varphi - \psi}{2}\right) = \frac{1}{2}\frac{\cos \varphi}{\cos \psi}\{1 + \cos (\varphi - \psi)\},$$

$$\frac{r^2\kappa^2}{\epsilon_1} = \frac{\cos \varphi}{\cos \psi} \sin^2\left(\frac{\varphi - \psi}{2}\right) = \frac{1}{2}\frac{\cos \varphi}{\cos \psi}\{1 - \cos (\varphi - \psi)\}.$$

These equations can easily be transformed into the functions of [68], remembering the definition of φ and ψ. The introduction of these angles is of some help in deriving additional results below in the text, which are given without proof.

In the interval $x = 0, \cdots x = \infty$, the square of the refractive index ranges from $r^2 = \epsilon_1, \cdots r^2 = \epsilon_0$; the product $r^2\kappa^2$ starts with 0 for $x = 0$, goes through a maximum and comes back to 0 again for $x = \infty$, and the same is true for the absorption index κ alone. Figure 26 shows this behavior in a special case. Some details may be of interest, from the standpoint of the description of an actual experiment.

The absorption index κ has a maximum for the frequency ω given by the formula

$$\omega\tau = \frac{\epsilon_0 + 2}{\epsilon_1 + 2}\sqrt{\frac{\epsilon_1}{\epsilon_0}}.$$

This maximum value itself is

$$\kappa_{\text{max.}} = \frac{\sqrt{\epsilon_1} - \sqrt{\epsilon_0}}{\sqrt{\epsilon_1} + \sqrt{\epsilon_0}}$$

and at the corresponding frequency the square of the refraction index is given as

$$r^2 = \frac{1}{2}\frac{\sqrt{\epsilon_0\epsilon_1}}{\epsilon_0 + \epsilon_1}(\sqrt{\epsilon_0} + \sqrt{\epsilon_1})^2.$$

In the special case of decidedly polar molecules for which ϵ_1 is large compared with ϵ_0, the frequency at which the maximum of κ occurs will be appreciably smaller than the characteristic frequency $1/\tau$ and the maximum value itself will be nearly equal to unity.

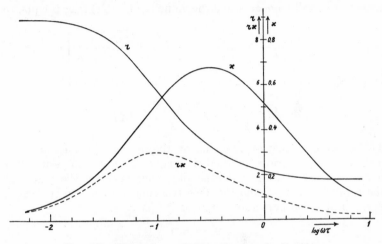

FIG. 26. Dispersion and absorption in polar liquids.

A distance of one wave-length (measured in the medium) is then sufficient to decrease the amplitude to $\epsilon^{-2\pi} = 1.85 \times 10^{-3}$ of its initial value. At this place in the spectrum the square of the refraction index is under the same conditions approximately equal to $\frac{1}{2}\sqrt{\epsilon_0\epsilon_1}$.

The product $r\kappa$ is the significant quantity in estimating the absorption if the range is measured in terms of the wave-length λ_0 measured in vacuum, for the amplitude of a wave after travelling over the distance s is proportional to $e^{-2\pi\kappa r(s/\lambda_0)}$. This product reaches its maximum value at a frequency different from that which makes κ a maximum; namely, if

$$\omega\tau = \frac{\epsilon_0 + 2}{\epsilon_1 + 2}\sqrt{\frac{3\epsilon_1 + \epsilon_0}{\epsilon_1 + 3\epsilon_0}},$$

and the maximum value is given by the expression

$$(r\kappa)_{\text{max.}} = \frac{\epsilon_1 - \epsilon_0}{2\sqrt{2(\epsilon_1 + \epsilon_0)}}.$$

At this place in the spectrum the square of the refractive index is

$$r^2 = \frac{(3\epsilon_1 + \epsilon_0)(\epsilon_1 + 3\epsilon_0)}{8(\epsilon_1 + \epsilon_0)},$$

which is nearly equal to $\frac{3}{8}\epsilon_1$, if $\epsilon_1 \gg \epsilon_0$.

To estimate the relaxation time τ from the experimentally obtained dispersion-curve for r_2 it is convenient to note that the square of the refraction index will be midway in its change from ϵ_1 to ϵ_0 (*i.e.*, will have acquired the value $(\epsilon_1 + \epsilon_0)/2$) if $\omega\tau$ is equal to

$$\omega\tau = \frac{\epsilon_0 + 2}{\epsilon_1 + 2} \sqrt{\frac{1}{2}\left[\frac{\epsilon_1 - \epsilon_0}{\epsilon_1 + \epsilon_0} + \sqrt{4 + \left(\frac{\epsilon_1 - \epsilon_0}{\epsilon_1 + \epsilon_0}\right)^2}\right]}.$$

In the special case that again $\epsilon_1 \gg \epsilon_0$, this equation yields

$$\frac{\epsilon_1 + 2}{\epsilon_0 + 2}\omega\tau = \sqrt{\frac{1 + \sqrt{5}}{2}} = 1.27.$$

The result of actual experiments on the absorption, measured for instance with a bridge method, is frequently given in terms of a phase angle Φ. If the potential difference between the plates of the condenser is $Ve^{i\omega t}$ and the dielectric constant ϵ has to be decomposed into a real part and an imaginary part

$$\epsilon = \epsilon' - i\epsilon'',$$

the charge Q on one of the plates (omitting constant factors) will be

$$Q = (\epsilon' - i\epsilon'')Ve^{i\omega t}$$

The phase angle can then be defined by the equation

$$\tan \Phi = \frac{\epsilon''}{\epsilon'}.$$

Going back to equations [66] and [67], it is easily seen that

$$\epsilon' = \epsilon_0 + \frac{\epsilon_1 - \epsilon_0}{1 + x^2},$$

$$\epsilon'' = \frac{(\epsilon_1 - \epsilon_0)}{1 + x^2}x,$$

and therefore

$$\tan \Phi = \frac{(\epsilon_1 - \epsilon_0)x}{\epsilon_1 + \epsilon_0 x^2}.$$

This phase angle reaches a maximum value at the same place in the spectrum where the absorption index κ is a maximum (x^2

$= \epsilon_1/\epsilon_0)$ and can be calculated at this place from the equation

$$\tan \Phi_{max.} = \frac{1}{2} \frac{\epsilon_1 - \epsilon_0}{\sqrt{\epsilon_1\epsilon_0}}.$$

At this frequency, for which $\kappa = \kappa_{max.}$, the two parts of ϵ are

$$\epsilon' = 2 \frac{\epsilon_1\epsilon_0}{\epsilon_1 + \epsilon_0} \quad \text{and} \quad \epsilon'' = \frac{\epsilon_1 - \epsilon_0}{\epsilon_1 + \epsilon_0} \sqrt{\epsilon_1\epsilon_0}.$$

19. Experiments on the Anomalous Dispersion and Absorption of Polar Liquids.

The weakest point in the theory presented in the foregoing Section 18 is the introduction of Mosotti's hypothesis, if the results are to be compared with actually existing experiments. These experiments have been performed with decidedly polar liquids. Now we know that these liquids always show association and it is very doubtful, indeed improbable, that we can make Mosotti's assumption about the internal field. We therefore should expect that the results of the actual experiments will deviate from the formula calculated for the ideal liquid treated in Section 18, although only in a quantitative and not in a qualitative way. However, if future experiments are made on dispersion, using sufficiently diluted solutions of polar molecules in non-polar liquids like benzene or hexane, we will then have a perfect right to apply the formulas to this case. Moreover it would be interesting from a purely experimental point of view to see how the characteristic region of anomalous dispersion shifts to longer wave-lengths, as we expect it to do, if the inner friction of the non-polar *solvent* is changed by lowering the temperature, or, for instance, by using a series of non-polar saturated hydrocarbons with increasing viscosities.

It is with these restrictions in mind that we are going to discuss some recent experiments of Mizushima,[7] which seem to be best to the point. Many former experiments of other investigators have given indications in the same direction, but are less complete.[8] According to our exposition the only new quantity entering in the equations for the description of anomalous dispersion and absorption was the product of the relaxation time τ and the frequency ω, as is seen, for instance, in equation [66]. This means that for these phenomena a correspondence law should hold stating that any effect of the frequency can likewise be obtained at constant frequency by

[7] San-ichiro Mizushima, *Bull. Chem. Soc. Japan*, **1**, 47, 83, 115, 143, 163 (1926); *Physik. Z.*, **28**, 418 (1927).

[8] O. v. Baeyer, *Ann. Physik*, **17**, 30 (1905); F. Eckert, *Verhandl. deut. physik. Ges.*, **15**, 307 (1913); H. Rubens, *ibid.*, **17**, 335 (1915); E. F. Nicholls and J. D. Tear, *Phys. Rev.*, **21**, 587 (1923); J. D. Tear, *Phys. Rev.*, **21**, 600 (1923); R. Bock, *Z. Physik*, **31**, 534 (1925).

making a corresponding change in τ.   Now τ was found to be equal
to $\zeta/2kT$ and by applying Stokes' calculation ζ was put equal to
$8\pi\eta a^3$.   The obvious variable in τ is therefore the temperature T
and, as we know that the inner friction constant η increases very
rapidly with decreasing temperature, we expect that τ will increase
still more rapidly under the same conditions.   We will therefore
expect that, if at a given constant temperature we have observed a
decrease of r^2 from ϵ_1 to ϵ_0 in going from low to high frequencies, a
similar curve of anomalous dispersion will be found if we do another
experiment in which we keep the frequency constant and observe r^2
with decreasing temperature.   Connected with the curve for r^2 is
the curve for the absorption index κ going from zero over a maximum
to zero again if the frequency changes from small to large values.
Keeping the frequency constant and changing the temperature from
high to low values should therefore give an absorption effect first
increasing to a maximum and afterwards decreasing again.   However, if experiments with variable frequency are compared with
experiments carried out for variable temperature, the curves although alike in general appearance will not be identical; for whereas
in the first kind of experiments ϵ_1 and ϵ_0 are constants, by changing
the temperature in the second experiment we not only change τ
but also ϵ_1 and ϵ_0.   A perfect similarity would only be possible if
experiments were made on a solution of a polar in a non-polar liquid
in such a way that the change in the relaxation time would be produced by changing the non-polar component at constant temperature.

Mizushima has measured the dielectric constant and the absorption in different alcohols for three different wave-lengths
$\lambda_0 = 3.08m$, $9.5m$, and $50m$, over a range of temperatures extending between $+60°$ and $-60°$ Centigrade.   In the discussion of his
measurements he has assumed that what he calls the dielectric
constant must be identified with r^2, the square of the refractivity
index.[9]   What he actually determined, however, is the real part ϵ'
and the imaginary part ϵ'' of the generalized dielectric constant
$\epsilon = \epsilon' - i\epsilon''$.   Expressed in r and κ these two quantities stand for
$\epsilon' = r^2(1 - \kappa^2)$ and $\epsilon'' = 2\kappa r^2$.   Applying [68], or, most simply,
in going back to the original equation [66], it is seen that, as we
calculated at the end of Section 18:

  [9] This is clear from the formula he uses, which is almost identical with the
first formula of [68] as is seen most simply by using the representation referred
to in small print.   The only difference is that he defines the relaxation time τ by
the formula $\tau = \zeta/kT$, whereas we find $\tau = \zeta/2kT$.   This difference is due to
the fact that Mizushima takes his formula from the 1913 publication [P. Debye,
Verhandl. deut. physik. Ges., 15, 777 (1913)] in which the fictitious case of molecules
rotating about a definite direction in space was treated.

$$\left.\begin{array}{l} \epsilon' = \dfrac{\epsilon_1 + \epsilon_0 x^2}{1 + x^2} = \epsilon_0 + \dfrac{\epsilon_1 - \epsilon_0}{1 + \cdot\left(\dfrac{\epsilon_1 + 2}{\epsilon_0 + 2}\right)^2 \omega^2 \tau^2}, \\[4mm] \epsilon'' = (\epsilon_1 - \epsilon_0)\dfrac{x}{1 + x^2} = (\epsilon_1 - \epsilon_0)\dfrac{\dfrac{\epsilon_1 + 2}{\epsilon_0 + 2}\cdot \omega\tau}{1 + \left(\dfrac{\epsilon_1 + 2}{\epsilon_0 + 2}\right)^2 \cdot \omega^2 \tau^2}. \end{array}\right\} \quad [69]$$

In fact if measurements are made with a bridge method or a resonance method, it is the custom to state the result in saying that the system is equivalent to a condenser having no losses and of capacity C shunted by a resistance W. In such a system a potential difference $V e^{i\omega t}$ will cause a current

$$\left(i\omega C + \frac{1}{W}\right) V e^{i\omega t} = i\omega\left(C - \frac{i}{\omega W}\right) V e^{i\omega t}.$$

On the other hand, if $\epsilon = \epsilon' - i\epsilon''$ is the generalized dielectric constant, the current is

$$\frac{d}{dt}(\epsilon C_0 V e^{i\omega t}) = i\omega(\epsilon' - i\epsilon'')C_0 V e^{i\omega t}$$

if C_0 is the capacity of the empty condenser. Comparing these two formulas, it is seen that the quotient C/C_0, which is commonly called the dielectric constant, is equal to ϵ', whereas ϵ'' is equal to $1/\omega W C_0$.[10] The method actually employed was a method of electrical resonance involving three circuits electromagnetically coupled.

The first circuit or driver circuit was adjusted to a definite frequency and the interaction with the other circuits was so small that the conditions in this circuit could be considered as constant throughout the whole experiment. The intermediate circuit could be tuned to this frequency by means of a standard variable condenser of capacity K, connected in parallel with another condenser of capacity X, which used as its dielectric the liquid under investigation. The third circuit or detector circuit was coupled to the intermediate circuit and contained a rectifier and galvanometer. The variable condenser K was first adjusted to bring the current in the detector circuit to its maximum value. This maximum indication S of the galvanometer was read. In order to investigate how the two readings K and S are connected with the dielectric constant and the absorption of the polar liquid, a set of auxiliary experiments was made, in which water or acetone was used as a dielectric. These

[10] If the system is compared with a pure capacity C and a resistance R in series, we have the relations

$$\epsilon' = \frac{C/C_0}{1 + \omega^2 R^2 C^2}, \qquad \epsilon'' = \frac{C}{C_0}\frac{\omega R C}{1 + \omega^2 R^2 C^2}.$$

liquids did not show any dispersion or absorption effect in the region of frequencies and temperatures under exploration. An absorption effect was then originated by dissolving a salt like KI or NaCl in the water or acetone. Walden's measurements [11] as well as some experiments of Mizushima himself show that, within the limits of precision obtained (some percent) and with the concentration actually used, there is practically no change of the dielectric constant due to the presence of the salt. It was found of course that dissolving the salt changed the current S from its maximum value S_0 (corresponding to the experiment with the pure liquid) to a smaller value S_1. Before reading S_1 the adjustment of the capacity K has to be corrected by a quantity Δ in order to re-establish the resonance condition. For different concentrations the specific conductivity Λ of the solution was measured in the usual way. Comparing different concentrations, different salts, and experiments using the two different liquids, water and acetone, it was found experimentally that the quotient S_1/S_0 was practically a function only of the conductivity Λ. The same was shown to hold for the correction Δ in the setting of the variable capacity K.

Assuming the validity of this rule under the actually existing experimental conditions, the way in which every experiment was discussed is the following.

At a given temperature and for a given wave-length the capacity K is set to induce a maximum current in the detector circuit of the value S_1. This value S_1 is compared with the value S_0 obtained for a non-absorbing liquid, and in a table connecting S_1/S_0 with Λ the corresponding value of Λ is read. In another table connecting Λ with the correction Δ the value Δ is read and used to correct the setting of K to the value it would have had if no absorption would have existed. This corrected value of K leads at once to the value of ϵ', the dielectric constant, whereas the absorption is expressed in terms of the equivalent conductivity Λ. In order to give some notions concerning the concentrations necessary for the different conductivities, Table XIV is given, applying to solutions of KI in acetone.

TABLE XIV. *Conductivities of KI Solutions in Acetone.*

Dilution in Liters per Mol.	Conductivity in cm.$^{-1}$ Ohm^{-1}
240	48×10^{-5}
480	26×10^{-5}
960	14×10^{-5}
1920	7×10^{-5}
3840	3.5×10^{-5}
7680	1.8×10^{-5}

[11] Walden, Z. physik. Chem., **115**, 177 (1925); **116**, 261 (1925).

The next table XV shows how the dielectric constant and the absorption in glycerin change with temperature for a constant frequency corresponding to $\lambda_0 = 9.5$ m.

TABLE XV. *Dielectric Constant and Absorption in Glycerin for Different Frequencies.*

Glycerin, $\lambda_0 = 9.5$ m.

Temperature	ϵ'	$\Lambda \times 10^5$	ϵ''
65	36	1	—
40	41	3	1.7
22	42	15	8.6
11	35	26	15
3	27	26	15
0	20	26	15
−11	12	11	6.3
−24	6	3	1.7
−41	5	1	0.6
−61	3	<1	—

The absorption has been expressed in the same way as Mizushima did, by reporting the equivalent conductivity, but it is easy to calculate the corresponding imaginary part ϵ'' of the generalized dielectric constant $\epsilon = \epsilon' - i\epsilon''$. Values for ϵ'' are given in the last column. In fact the resistance of a condenser with the capacity C_0 in vacuum, filled with a liquid of conductivity Λ, is

$$W = \frac{1}{9 \times 10^{11}} \times \frac{1}{\Lambda} \frac{1}{4\pi C_0} \text{ e.s.u.}$$

if Λ is measured in Ohm^{-1} cm.$^{-1}$, C_0 in cm., and the factor $1/(9 \times 10^{11})$ is introduced to revert to electrostatic units.

The equation holds for any form of the condenser. We will not give the general proof, but just refer to the special case of a condenser consisting of two parallel plates of surface f at a distance l apart. If filled with a liquid of conductivity Λ, the resistance in ohms will be

$$W = \frac{l}{\Lambda}\frac{1}{f} = \frac{1}{4\pi} \times \frac{1}{\Lambda} \times \frac{4\pi l}{f},$$

and $f/4\pi l$ is the electrostatic capacity of the system in vacuum.

The current in such a condenser under the influence of the potential difference $Ve^{i\omega t}$ will be

$$\left(i\omega C + \frac{1}{W} \right) Ve^{i\omega t} = i\omega \left(C - i\, 9 \times 10^{11} \frac{4\pi \Lambda C_0}{\omega} \right) Ve^{i\omega t}.$$

Since $C/C_0 = \epsilon'$, this formula shows that

$$\epsilon'' = 9.\times 10^{11} \frac{4\pi \Lambda}{\omega},$$

or introducing the wave-length λ_0 in vacuum, measured in cm.:

$$\epsilon'' = 60\lambda_0\Lambda. \qquad [70]$$

It is with the help of this formula that we have expressed the equivalent conductivity Λ in terms of ϵ''.

In a general way the numerical values of Table XV behave as if they could be calculated using the formulas [69] and varying x from small to large values in going from high to low temperatures. There is, however, one departure insofar as ϵ' first increases with decreasing temperature for higher temperatures. This fact is due to the change of the "constants" ϵ_1 and ϵ_0, which we discussed on page 96.

The following table XVI contains measurements of the same kind and for the same wave-length $\lambda_0 = 9.5$ m., with the five alcohols: methyl, ethyl, isopropyl, isobutyl and amyl alcohol. The values of Λ have been converted into values for the imaginary part ϵ'' of the dielectric constant using equation [70].

TABLE XVI.   *Dispersion and Absorption for Different Temperatures.*

$(\lambda_0 = 9.5 \text{ m.})$

Temperature °C.	Methyl alcohol		Ethyl alcohol		Isopropyl alcohol		Isobutyl alcohol		Amyl alcohol	
	ϵ'	ϵ''	ϵ'	ϵ''	ϵ'	ϵ''	ϵ'	ϵ''	ϵ'	ϵ''
60	—	—	—	—	15	0	14	0	11	0
40	31	1	22	0.6	17	0	16	0	13	0
20	34	1	25	1.1	21	1.1	19	1.9	16	1.1
0	37	1	28	1.5	24	2.3	20	6.1	17	4.6
−20	40	1.5	31	2.9	24	8.5	11	11	10	5.7
−40	45	2.3	33	8.0	13	11	5	5	5	2.3
−60	51	7.4	24	22	6	71	4	1.1	4	1.1

Over the whole interval of temperature, ϵ' increases with decreasing temperature for methyl alcohol; this substance therefore does not yet show the peculiar effect we expect, for a wave as long as 9.5 m. The same wave-length, however, is sufficiently small to bring the whole dispersion curve within the range of the temperature interval for a substance like amyl alcohol. The alcohols in between show how the transition occurs. With the dispersion is connected the absorption measured by ϵ'', and, as we expect (see [69]), it is zero for high *and* low temperatures and has a maximum for an intermediate temperature, in the case of amyl alcohol. In the other extreme case of methyl alcohol the absorption just starts at the lower end of the temperature interval.

As a last example Table XVII is given, containing values of ϵ' and ϵ'' for one substance, normal propyl alcohol, now however not only for one but for three wave-lengths and different temperatures t measured in degrees Centigrade. The values of ϵ'' have again been calculated by equation [70]. The table contains, moreover, the values of the inner friction constant η for different temperatures.

TABLE XVII. *Dispersion and Absorption for n-Propyl Alcohol.*

$$a = 2.2 \times 10^{-8} \text{ cm.}$$

t °C.	η	$\lambda_0 = 50$ m.		$\lambda_0 = 9.5$ m.		$\lambda_0 = 3.08$ m.	
		ϵ'	ϵ''	ϵ'	ϵ''	ϵ'	ϵ''
60	—	—	—	16 (−)	—	17 (−)	0.5 (−)
40	—	18.5 (−)	—	19 (−)	—	19 (−)	1.5 (−)
20	0.0226	21.5 (22)	—	22 (22)	1 (2)	20.5 (21)	4 (5)
0	0.0388	24 (25)	—	25 (24)	3 (4)	17.5 (20)	9 (10)
−20	0.0716	27.5 (27.5)	—	24 (24)	8 (8.5)	11 (13)	9 (13)
−40	0.154	30 (29)	4 (5.5)	15 (15.5)	13 (14)	6.5 (4.5)	4 (8)
−60	0.368	24 (26)	14 (13)	7 (5)	7 (10)	5 (2.5)	2 (3.5)

If we read this table in a horizontal direction, we see at $+20°$ just a faint beginning of anomalous dispersion for $\lambda_0 = 3.08$ m. At $-40°$, on the contrary, nearly the whole dispersion curve is contained in the interval ranging from $\lambda_0 = 50$ m. to $\lambda_0 = 3.08$ m., since the dielectric constant ϵ' drops from 30 to 15 to 6.5. At the same time ϵ'' goes from 4 over the high value 13 to a small value 4 again. If we read the table in a vertical direction, we see for the wave-length $\lambda_0 = 50$ m. just a beginning of a decrease in ϵ' for $-60°$. For the smaller wave-length $\lambda_0 = 3.08$ m. the dielectric constant drops to the small value 5 at the lowest temperature of $-60°$. In the temperature range from $+60°$ to $-60°$ the quantity ϵ'' has first increased to a maximum, reached at approximately $-20°$, and fallen again to 2 at $-60°$.

Figure 27 is given to fix in the mind the numerical results contained in Table XVII. One last thing is left; that is, the discussion of the absolute value of the relaxation time. According to the theory ϵ' and ϵ'' should be represented by [69] and, accepting the rotating sphere of radius a as a picture of the molecule, the relaxation time should be represented according to [60] and [52] by the formula

$$\tau = 4\pi \frac{\eta a^3}{kT}.$$

Assuming for a the value [12]

$$a = 2.2 \times 10^{-8} \text{ cm.}$$

and introducing for η the values of the inner friction constant given in the table, the values in brackets contained in the table were calculated, applying equation [69]. It is seen that the experimental

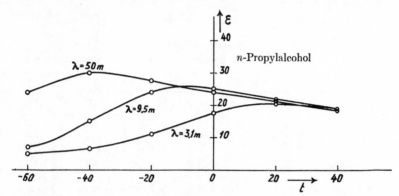

FIG. 27.   Variation of dispersion in polar liquids with temperature.

results are fairly well represented, even though the application of Mosotti's hypothesis and the neglect of the association have introduced some errors, and notwithstanding the crudeness of the sphere as a picture of the molecule. Also for the other alcohols the necessary values of a are reasonable. We ought, however, to expect some difficulties in carrying our calculations this far, and it is reassuring to see them come up in the case of glycerin, where a would have to be taken equal 0.35×10^{-8} cm., following Mizushima's calculation. Correcting his error will not eliminate the fact that the radius will still come out smaller than we would infer from the dimensions of the molecule. It would be interesting to do experiments on solutions of glycerin in a non-polar liquid in order to see how much of this difficulty is due to the neglected association.

20. Anomalous Dispersion and Absorption in Solids.

In 1924 J. Errera [13] published experiments on the dielectric constant of solids for temperatures in the neighborhood of their melting point. As he states his results, he found that solids which after melting give polar liquids show anomalous dispersion even in the solid state. For solids consisting of non-polar molecules he

[12] In his paper Mizushima gives $a = 2.0 \times 10^{-8}$, but we had to recalculate because, as was already pointed out, he compares the observed values with r^2 instead of $r^2(1 - \kappa^2)$.

[13] J. Errera, J. phys., (6) 5, 304 (1924).

found no appreciable dispersion within the range of radio frequencies. His results have recently been confirmed for ice by experiments of Wintsch carried out in my own laboratory.   In Figure 28

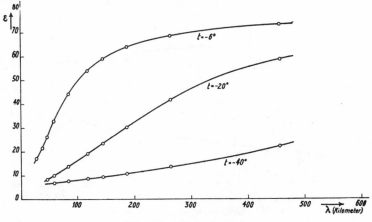

FIG. 28.   Dispersion in ice.

some of his curves are given, showing the change of the dielectric constant with frequency for three different temperatures.   They are very much like the curves for polar liquids and resemble them also with respect to the influence of temperature, as the characteristic wave-length for which the dispersion is most noticeable increases rapidly with decreasing temperature.   The only difference is a quantitative one.   The dielectric constant of ice at $-6°$ Centigrade has dropped as low as 40 for the relatively long wave-length of approximately 70 kilometers, whereas the higher liquid alcohols discussed in the foregoing Section have their dispersion region for some meters and liquid water even for some centimeters of wavelength.   It may be said that a solid like ice behaves as if it were a polar liquid with very high inner friction.   The similarity exists in the behavior of the absorption also, for a relatively strong dielectric absorption accompanies the dispersion of the ordinary dielectric constant.   This is shown in Figure 29 in which are plotted the dielectric constant and the phase angle measured for ice at one temperature ($t = -40°$) and different frequencies.   If we think of the picture of crystals, derived by the X-ray method, in which the individual atoms are arranged in inter-penetrating lattices, it is difficult to understand why the similarity between liquid and solid should exist.   For it does not seem admissible to speak of *molecules* in a crystal, which can turn in all different directions in space encountering only frictional forces.

If, however, we accept Errera's statement, we certainly have to look upon a molecule as preserving its individuality to some extent even in a solid, for the polarity is a property intimately connected with the arrangement of the atoms in the single molecule. If this is granted it can be shown that a very limited degree of freedom for

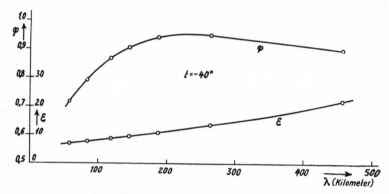

FIG. 29. Dispersion and absorption in ice.

the orientation of the molecules in a crystal will be sufficient to explain the observed anomalous dispersion. How this can be done may be elucidated with the help of the following crude picture. Suppose a constant field F acting on a number of molecules, each having the moment μ and situated, for instance, at the intersection points of a space lattice. Let us further suppose that each molecule can point with its moment only in two definite directions, the direction of F and the opposite direction. We will call the direction of F the positive direction, and refer to the group of molecules pointing in this direction as the positive group, whereas the group pointing in the opposite direction will be called the negative group. Between these two groups there will be an interchange of molecules, due partly to the heat motions and partly to the action of the field. We try to describe this interchange in a formal way. Let us call the number of particles in the positive group n_1 and in the negative group n_2 and fix our attention on the first group. The change in number during the time δt will be $(dn_1/dt)\delta t$, and will consist of two parts: a negative part for the particles leaving group 1 and a positive part for the particles entering the group. If the probability that one particle considered during one second makes the transition from group 1 to group 2 is w_{12}, the negative part is $w_{12}n_1\delta t$. The positive part can be calculated as $w_{21}n_2\delta t$, introducing the corresponding probability w_{21} for the transition from group 2 to group 1. Since a reasoning of the same kind can be applied to the particles of the second group, we have

$$\left.\begin{aligned}
\frac{dn_1}{dt} &= - w_{12}n_1 + w_{21}n_2, \\
\frac{dn_2}{dt} &= + w_{12}n_1 - w_{21}n_2.
\end{aligned}\right\} \qquad [71]$$

In case of equilibrium, where $dn_1/dt = dn_2/dt = 0$, we derive from [71] the condition

$$\frac{w_{12}}{w_{21}} = \frac{n_2}{n_1}. \qquad [72]$$

But in this case we know that Boltzmann's distribution function holds, which gives

$$n_1 = A e^{\mu F/kT} \qquad \text{and} \qquad n_2 = A e^{-(\mu F/kT)}.$$

Therefore according to equation [72]

$$w_{12} = \frac{1}{2\tau} e^{-(\mu F/kT)} \qquad \text{and} \qquad w_{21} = \frac{1}{2\tau} e^{\mu F/kT}, \qquad [73]$$

where τ is any function of T and F. If we can confine our attention to such field intensities that $\mu F/kT$ is small, the equations [71] can then be written in the form

$$\left.\begin{aligned}
2\tau \frac{dn_1}{dt} &= - (n_1 - n_2) + \frac{\mu F}{kT} (n_1 + n_2), \\
2\tau \frac{dn_2}{dt} &= (n_1 - n_2) - \frac{\mu F}{kT} (n_1 + n_2).
\end{aligned}\right\} \qquad [74]$$

Although only derived for a constant field intensity F, we may suppose that these equations will still hold if F is variable. If we do this, then we have obtained an equivalent of the equations of the Brownian movement, used in the foregoing sections. Suppose now a periodic field

$$F = F_0 e^{i\omega t},$$

and try the solution

$$\left.\begin{aligned}
n_1 &= n_0 + \nu_0 e^{i\omega t}, \\
n_2 &= n_0 - \nu_0 e^{i\omega t}
\end{aligned}\right\} \qquad [75]$$

(which makes $n_1 = n_2$ for $\nu_0 = 0$), considering ν_0 as a small quantity of the order of $\mu F_0/kT$. It is readily seen that [75] is consistent with [74] providing

$$\nu_0 = \frac{n_0}{1 + i\omega\tau} \frac{\mu F_0}{kT}. \qquad [75']$$

The quantity τ now plays the part of a relaxation time and since in equation [74] it occurs only multiplied with quantities of the order of magnitude ν_0, and therefore of F_0, it can be considered as a function of the temperature only. From [75] and [75'] it follows that the average electric moment of a molecule in the direction of F will be

$$\overline{m} = \frac{1}{1 + i\omega\tau} \frac{\mu^2 F_0}{kT} e^{i\omega t}, \qquad [76]$$

as is seen at once, observing that the moment of $2n_0$ molecules will be

$$(n_0 + \nu_0 e^{i\omega t})\mu - (n_0 - \nu_0 e^{i\omega t})\mu.$$

Except for the factor 1/3 the expression [76] is the same as was found in the case of a liquid. The difference in the numerical factor is of course due to the fact that in this section we considered only the directions parallel to F and supposed no other directions to be possible. Although [76] is formally identical with the former result, we learn much less than in the case of liquids, because the question as to the dependence of τ on the temperature has not been touched.

To realize how many molecules have to be turned in a statical field ($\omega = 0$) let us take the case of ice and assume the dielectric constant to be 80. In a field of the intensity 1 volt/cm. every cc. will then acquire an electric moment $I = 0.021$ e.s.u. Suppose now that this polarization is due to orientation alone and let us adopt our picture of only two possible directions for the permanent moments. As the electric moment of one H_2O-molecule is equal to 1.87×10^{-18} e.s.u., it is sufficient if in every cc. 0.56×10^{16} molecules have turned from group 2 to group 1. But the total number of molecules contained in 1 cc. is 3×10^{22}, so in the average we have then turned one molecule in every five million. Looking at these figures, it does not seem so extremely improbable that we can accept such a slight disarrangement even in a crystal, without fearing to upset the crystalline structure practically.

If we adopt equation [76] for the average moment due to orientation and assume the validity of Mosotti's hypothesis regarding the internal field, it means that we should be able to calculate the generalized dielectric constant $\epsilon = \epsilon' - i\epsilon''$ by the same formulas [69] which we used for liquids:

$$\left. \begin{array}{l} \epsilon' = \epsilon_0 + \dfrac{\epsilon_1 - \epsilon_0}{1 + \left(\dfrac{\epsilon_1 + 2}{\epsilon_0 + 2}\right)^2 \omega^2\tau^2}, \\[4ex] \epsilon'' = (\epsilon_1 - \epsilon_0) \dfrac{\dfrac{\epsilon_1 + 2}{\epsilon_0 + 2}\omega\tau}{1 + \left(\dfrac{\epsilon_1 + 2}{\epsilon_0 + 2}\right)^2 \omega^2\tau^2}. \end{array} \right\} \qquad [77]$$

Adopting the values $\epsilon_0 = 2.2$ and $\epsilon_1 = 80$ for a temperature of $t = -2°$, it is seen from Table XVIII, containing experimental values determined by Errera, that ϵ' will be equal 41.1 (that is, half way from 80 to 2.2) for a wave-length of approximately 82 kilometers. The first of the equations [77] shows then that at this place of the spectrum $\omega\tau$ has to be put equal to

$$\omega\tau = \frac{\epsilon_0 + 2}{\epsilon_1 + 2} = 0.051,$$

and, as $\omega = 0.230 \times 10^5$, this implies

$$\tau = 2.2 \times 10^{-6} \text{ sec.}$$

This time represents also an estimate of the average time a molecule belongs to one of the groups of our picture. It is of course very large in comparison with the time of vibration of a molecule in the crystal-lattice. Adopting the round values $\tau = 2 \times 10^{-6}$ sec., $\epsilon_0 = 2.2$, $\epsilon_1 = 80$, the values of ϵ' and ϵ'' have been calculated for different wave-lengths according to [77] and are given in Table XVIII together with the experimental values of ϵ' determined by Errera.

TABLE XVIII.   *Dispersion and Absorption for Ice at* $-2°$ *Centigrade.*

λ Kilometers	ϵ' experimental	ϵ' calculated	ϵ'' calculated	Φ calculated
0	—	2.2	0	0°
8	4.6	3	9	70.5°
18.5	7.8	7	19	69°
28.5	15.2	13	27	64°
38.5	23.2	20	33	58°
54	30.6	31	38	50.5°
97	47.2	53	37	34.5°
196	69	71	25	19°
294	73.4	76	17	13°
465	76	78	11	8.5°
680	77.3	79	8	6°
∞	—	80	0	0°

No attempt was made to fit the constants for the best possible representation of the observed values; therefore the impression prevails that after all a formula of the kind of [77] and a picture as the one proposed may be what is needed. A special feature of the theory is that every dispersion has to be accompanied by absorption, to be measured by the imaginary part of ϵ. We include in the table values for ϵ'' calculated by the second equation [77] and the phase angle corresponding to this absorption defined by the equation

$$\tan \Phi = \frac{\epsilon''}{\epsilon'}.$$

Such an absorption certainly exists for ice and the phase angle has been measured by J. Granier [14] and by Wintsch. In Granier's experiments Φ reached a maximum of 68° for a wave-length between 17 and 55 kilometers. The tentative theory set forward considers the substance as absolutely nonconductive. If some conductivity exists, it has therefore to be expected that for low frequencies this conductivity may create an absorption not accounted for by [77].

Finally we give some values of the relaxation time, first for liquid normal propyl alcohol at different temperatures,

$$t = 20° \quad 0° \quad -20° \quad -40° \quad -60°$$

$$\tau \times 10^{10} = 0.9 \quad 1.6 \quad 3.2 \quad 7.4 \quad 26 \text{ seconds}$$

and secondly for ice,

$$t = -5° \quad -22°$$

$$\tau \times 10^6 = 2.7 \quad 18 \text{ seconds}$$

It is seen how this relaxation time increases in both cases very rapidly with decreasing temperature and that τ in the solid is some 10,000 times larger than the relaxation time in the liquid. As an analogy applicable to a certain extent, also with respect to the picture, the difference in rate of diffusion in liquids and solids may be quoted.

[14] J. Granier, *Compt. rend.*, **179**, 1314 (1924).

CHAPTER VI

ELECTRICAL SATURATION EFFECTS

21. The Dielectric Constant in Strong Electric Fields.

Our treatment of the orientation of polar molecules in a constant field F has shown that the mean moment of a molecule is expressed by the equation

$$\overline{m} = \mu L\left(\frac{\mu F}{kT}\right),$$

where L is the Langevin function defined by

$$L(x) = \coth x - \frac{1}{x}.$$

Here we see that the mean moment is not a linear function for large values of the argument, and for such values the dielectric constant would not be a true constant but would depend upon the field intensity. If, therefore, measurements of the dielectric constant would be carried out, say with an oscillating field of small intensity, it should make a difference if this is the only field or if a strong constant field is superposed. In the last case we should expect a diminution of the dielectric constant, as the superposed field alone would bring the mean moment appreciably nearer to the saturation value. Experiments were made by Ratnowsky [1] and by Herweg.[2] Herweg comes to the conclusion that the effect exists in liquid ethyl ether, which is indeed polar. The immediate result of the experiment has to be corrected for the electro-striction accompanying the action of the intense constant field. But even if this correction has been taken account of, as Herweg did, we cannot neglect entirely a second contribution to the effect; namely, the property of molecules to become oriented even though they are entirely non-polar. Following the discussion in Section 8, we found that with respect to its distortion any molecule can be represented by an ellipsoid, or, in other words, by three principal polarizabilities related to three perpendicular axes. So, if such a molecule is placed in a field, the orientation for which the axis of highest polarizability is parallel to the field will be an orientation of smallest potential energy. Therefore there will exist an orientation effect, dependent on the temper-

[1] S. Ratnowsky, *Verhandl. deut. physik. Ges.*, **15**, 497 (1913).
[2] J. Herweg, *Z. Physik*, **3**, 36 (1920); J. Herweg and W. Pötzsch, *ibid.*, **8**, 1 (1922).

ature, which vanishes only if there is no direction of preference in the molecule.   One method for investigating this orientation would consist in passing light through the substance in a direction perpendicular to the constant field, with two different directions of vibration, the first parallel to the field and the second perpendicular to the field.   The velocities of these two differently polarized lightrays should then be different.   This effect is known as the Kerreffect [3] and other texts contain an outline of the theory as given by Langevin.[4]   In the preceding part of this book we did not take this orientation into account at all.   A sufficient reason for this is that this effect is proportional to the square of the field intensity, and therefore can play no role at all in ordinary measurements of the dielectric constant.   Very recently an experimental investigation of the saturation-effect was published by Kautzsch.[5]   His substances were ethyl ether, chloroform, monochlorobenzene, carbon disulfide and hexane.   Only the first three are polar molecules.   Kautzsch, taking account of the influence of the Kerr-effect, shows that for the first three substances the dielectric constant diminishes in strong fields, as expected.   For carbon disulfide, a non-polar substance, he finds a slight increase.   This, however, can be shown to be a natural result of the orientation responsible for the Kerr-effect.   Finally in the non-polar hexane no change at all could be measured.

For the ordinary available field strengths the effect is small, 25,000 volts/cm. giving a relative change in dielectric constant of approximately 2×10^{-5}.   This is what we should expect from the picture and the known values of the electric moments.   To illustrate this point the following calculation is given.

Let us assume that the three principal polarizabilities are equal to each other and ask how the dielectric constant will depend, to a first approximation, on the intensity X of the constant field.   If we adopt Mosotti's hypothesis, we will have the three equations

$$\left. \begin{aligned} D &= X + 4\pi I, \\ F &= X + \frac{4\pi}{3} I, \\ I &= n \left[\alpha_0 F + \mu L \left(\frac{\mu F}{kT} \right) \right], \end{aligned} \right\} \qquad [78]$$

where n denotes the number of molecules per cc.   These equations will enable us to eliminate F and I and to express D in terms of X. To a small change δX of X will correspond a change δD of D, and the quotient $\delta D / \delta X$ will be what has to be called the dielectric con-

[3] J. Kerr, *Phil. Mag.*, (4) **50**, 337, 446 (1875).
[4] P. Langevin, *Le Radium*, **7**, 249 (1910); for more particulars see P. Debye, "Handb. d. Radiologie," **VI**, p. 754.
[5] F. Kautzsch, *Physik. Z.*, **29**, 105 (1928).

stant ϵ with the field X present. To a second approximation the result of this calculation is

$$\epsilon = \bar{\epsilon} - \frac{4\pi}{15}\left(\frac{\bar{\epsilon}+2}{3}\right)^4 \frac{n\mu^2}{kT}\left(\frac{\mu X}{kT}\right)^2 \qquad [79].$$

if $\bar{\epsilon}$ is the ordinary dielectric constant for small field intensity.[6] Let us take ethyl ether as an example, neglecting the Kerr-effect. In this case

$$\bar{\epsilon} = 4.30, \quad n = 5.83 \times 10^{21}, \quad \mu = 1.22 \times 10^{-18},$$

and, putting $T = 293$, it is found

$$\epsilon = 4.30 - 0.327 \times 10^{-8}X^2.$$

In order to change ϵ by 1 part in 10^5 the applied intensity should be

$$X = 115 \text{ e.s.u.} = 35,000 \text{ volts/cm.}$$

In the case of an associating liquid like water, for instance, it is very doubtful if we can apply Mosotti's hypothesis. In such a case therefore the calculated value of X can be nothing more than a very rough estimate. But the calculation in accordance with the experiment certainly shows that appreciable changes in the dielectric constant can only be expected in very intense fields.[7]

22. Dielectric Constant of Ionic Solutions.[8]

As we learn from the figure at the end of the foregoing section, in ordinary circumstances we are not concerned with electrical saturation effects. If, on the other hand, we have a solution containing ions, extremely high fields may exist in the neighborhoods of the ions, and in such cases these electrical saturation effects are of importance. Let us consider such a case in greater detail, supposing for instance that our liquid is water which contains a certain number of ions. Thus a single ion would give rise to the field intensity

$$E = \frac{e}{\epsilon r^2},$$

[6] For details and the general formula taking into account the Kerr-effect, as well as the interaction of this effect with the polar effect, see P. Debye, "Handb. d. Radiologie," *loc. cit.*

[7] F. Malsch, *Ann. Physik*, **84**, 841 (1927), did not find so large an effect for water as the application of Mosotti's hypothesis would lead us to expect.

[8] In the last years this subject has been treated by different authors. The general lines of treatment are the same, but the experimental results are not consistent enough. *Compare* P. Walden and H. Ulich, *Z. physik. Chem.*, **110**, 44 (1924); P. Walden and O. Werner, *ibid.*, **116**, 261 (1925); O. Blüh, *Z. Physik*, **25**, 220 (1924); H. Schmick, *ibid.*, **24**, 56 (1924); H. Hellmann and H. Zahn, *Physik. Z.*, **27**, 636 (1926); *Ann. Physik*, **81**, 711 (1926); H. Sack, *Physik. Z.*, **27**, 206 (1926); **28**, 199 (1927); P. Pechhold, *Ann. Physik*, **83**, 427 (1927); R. Skanke and E. Schreiner, *Physik. Z.*, **28**, 597 (1927).

where e is the ionic charge and r is the distance from the centre of the ion. Thus, if we take $r = 10^{-7}$ cm., $\epsilon = 80$ and $e = 4.77 \times 10^{-10}$, this gives $E = 600$ e.s.u. or 180,000 volts per centimeter, which is great enough to cause an appreciable saturation effect. If, therefore, the water contains a number of ions, there will be a region around each ion which contains electrically saturated water. If now we superpose a small homogenous external field in order to measure the dielectric constant of the electrolyte solution, the regions of the water surrounding the ions will be made more or less inactive due to their saturation. A very rough picture of this occurrence will be obtained if each ion with its surrounding water is replaced by a spherical cavity, the radius of which depends on the distance over which the saturation effect is appreciable. Let us call the radius of each cavity a and consider the influence of a number n of such cavities per cc. on the dielectric constant. The question as to how a is connected with the saturation effect remains to be dealt with in the next section.

As a first step in the solution of this problem we will calculate the potential within and in the neighborhood of a single cavity. In the region external to the cavity at a distance r from the center the potential is

$$\varphi_a = -Ex + \frac{Ax}{r^3} = -\left(Er - \frac{A}{r^2} \right) \cos \vartheta, \qquad [80]$$

where the x-axis is taken in the direction of the electric force E, ϑ is the angle between this axis and r, and A is a properly chosen constant. The first term of the right-hand member is due to the external field and the second term is due to the cavity. Inside the cavity the potential is

$$\varphi_i = -Bx, \qquad [80']$$

where B is a constant. The constants A and B must be determined from the conditions at the boundary of the cavity which are

$$\varphi_a = \varphi_i; \quad r = a,$$

$$\epsilon_a \frac{\partial \varphi_a}{\partial r} = \epsilon_i \frac{\partial \varphi_i}{\partial r}; \quad r = a,$$

if ϵ_a and ϵ_i are the dielectric constants outside and inside the cavity. With the aid of these equations together with [80] and [80'] it is readily shown that

$$A = \frac{\epsilon_i - \epsilon_a}{\epsilon_i + 2\epsilon_a} E \times a^3; \quad B = \frac{3\epsilon_a}{\epsilon_i + 2\epsilon_a} \times E. \qquad [81]$$

Let us take a relatively large volume V containing only one cavity. The interior of the cavity is homogeneously polarized according to

[80'], the field intensity is B, and as the susceptibility is $(\epsilon_i - 1)/4\pi$, the total electric moment is

$$\frac{4\pi}{3} a^3 \frac{\epsilon_i - 1}{4\pi} \frac{3\epsilon_a}{\epsilon_i + 2\epsilon_a} \times E.$$

The total electric moment of the exterior region due to the homogeneous field E is

$$\left(V - \frac{4\pi}{3} a^3 \right) \frac{\epsilon_a - 1}{4\pi} E,$$

and the total electric moment corresponding to the field characterized by the second term of [80] is zero; for, the electric intensity in the x-direction derived from this part of the potential is

$$- A \left(\frac{1}{r^3} - 3 \frac{x^2}{r^5} \right).$$

This is proportional to the polarization in the same direction, and if we integrate this expression over a sphere it gives zero, because the mean value of x^2 on the sphere is equal to $r^2/3$. Therefore the total moment of the volume V will be

$$V \frac{\epsilon_a - 1}{4\pi} E + \frac{4\pi}{3} a^3 \left[\frac{\epsilon_i - 1}{4\pi} \frac{3\epsilon_a}{\epsilon_i + 2\epsilon_a} - \frac{\epsilon_a - 1}{4\pi} \right] E. \qquad [82]$$

Now suppose that n ions are dissolved per cc. and that the same size of cavity may correspond to each ion. For small concentrations we may then take $V = 1/n$ and calculate by [82] the electric moment of the space corresponding to one ion. Such being the case, then we will find the electric moment of 1 cc. of the solution, which we called the polarization I, in multiplying [82] with n, giving

$$I = \frac{\epsilon_a - 1}{4\pi} E + n \frac{4\pi}{3} a^3 \left[\frac{\epsilon_i - 1}{4\pi} \frac{3\epsilon_a}{\epsilon_i + 2\epsilon_a} - \frac{\epsilon_a - 1}{4\pi} \right] E.$$

But

$$D = E + 4\pi I,$$

and calling ϵ^* the apparent dielectric constant of the solution we will have

$$D = \epsilon^* E.$$

Combining these formulas, the result is

$$\epsilon^* = \epsilon_a + n \frac{4\pi}{3} a^3 (\epsilon_i - \epsilon_a) \frac{1 + 2\epsilon_a}{\epsilon_i + 2\epsilon_a}. \qquad [83]$$

We will compare the action of an ion with that of an empty cavity and therefore take $\epsilon_i = 1$, and at the same time we will from now on call the dielectric constant of the pure solvent ϵ instead of ϵ_a. In this special case [83] assumes the form

$$\epsilon^* = \epsilon \left[1 - \frac{\epsilon - 1}{\epsilon} n \frac{4\pi}{3} a^3 \right]. \qquad [83']$$

For small concentrations experiments show that the apparent dielectric constant *diminishes* with increasing concentration and may be expressed by an equation of the form

$$\epsilon^* = \epsilon(1 - \gamma C), \qquad [84]$$

where c denotes the concentration in mols per liter and γ is a constant characteristic for the salt and the solvent. The decrease of ϵ^* with increasing concentration is indeed accounted for by the saturation. At higher concentrations it is found that the dielectric constant comes back to, and surpasses, the value for the pure solvent. The qualitative picture proposed to explain this concentration effect is that, at higher concentrations, an appreciable number of doublets may be formed by the coupling of positive and negative ions, and that these doublets will give an increase in the dielectric constant by their orientation. The question of a chemical interaction, resulting in a relatively permanent and definite coupling, being necessary, or of the coupling due to the interionic electric forces being sufficient, has not yet been treated.[9] We will confine our attention to small concentrations for which the linear relation [84] holds, and adopt Sack's values, although we are aware that the differences in the absolute values found by different authors are so large that our conclusions are very preliminary and only can point out the direction for further experimental research. In the case of KCl Sack found, for instance, the values of γ contained in Table XIX corresponding to the different concentrations in mols per liter.

TABLE XIX.   *Dielectric Constant and Concentration (KCl Solutions).*

$c \times 10^3$	ϵ^*	γ
0.32	80.58	10.9
0.50	80.60	6.1
0.65	80.53	2.9
0.75	80.36	8.1
1.00	80.25	7.4
1.30	80.22	5.9

[9] Some remarks regarding this question have recently been made by P. Debye and H. Falkenhagen, *Physik. Z.*, **29**, 121 (1928). It is shown that such an interionic coupling exists in completely ionized solutions.

For pure water Sack finds at the same temperature (18° C.)

$$\epsilon = 80.85 \pm 0.08.$$

The difference between ϵ and ϵ^* is seen to be very small, and the error in the coefficient γ of [84] becomes larger the smaller the concentration. The calculated values of γ are contained in the third column, their weighted average being

$$\gamma = 6.9 \pm 1.0.$$

If we adopt this value, it means that 1 milli-mol of KCl per liter will give a decrease in the dielectric constant of 0.7 per cent. The number of ions present is then $n = 12 \times 10^{17}$ per cc. Applying equation [83'] will give us the radius of the equivalent cavities, which is found to be

$$a = 11 \times 10^{-8} \text{ cm.}$$

This value seems very large as compared with the dimensions of the ions, especially if it is remembered that we are to compare not a and the radius of the ion, but rather the third powers of these quantities. If the effect of uncharged dissolved molecules on the dielectric constant of the water is compared with the effect of cavities, in the same way as for ions, the radii are not so conspicuous (*e.g.*, about 3×10^{-8} cm. for sugar in water). It is therefore probable that the ionic charge has an electrical effect on the surrounding water extending to a relatively large distance, and that this effect can be represented as a saturation.[10]

23. Theory of Ionic Saturation.

The radius of the cavities introduced in the foregoing Section 22 is a quantity merely used in order to have a simple measure for the description of the peculiar state of the solvent surrounding the ion. In reality a sphere of which the inside is absolutely saturated and the outside is unchanged does not exist. A gradual change of the susceptibility will extend from the ion to any distance, increasing with decreasing distance. It seems a matter of importance to investigate if a purely electrical saturation effect will be strong enough to account for the changes in dielectric constant actually measured. Or in other words does the saturation theory enable us to make an estimate of actual size of the cavities representing the action of ions? With this question a second question presents itself at once; namely, how does the effect depend on the properties, especially on the charge, of the ions? These questions have been treated by Sack for a dielectric solvent in which Mosotti's hypothesis

[10] The connection of this electric saturation and what is commonly called hydration has been treated by T. J. Webb, *J. Am. Chem. Soc.*, **48**, 2589 (1926).

concerning the internal field is supposed to hold and whose molecules are supposed to have an invariable optical polarizability in all
directions.   Let us consider a small element of volume of the liquid
situated at a distance r from a given ion.   We ask what is the
dielectric constant of this element in the presence of a small external
field superposed on that of the ion.   First we consider only the field
set up by the ion.   We have the general equations

$$\left. \begin{array}{l} D = E + 4\pi I, \\[2mm] F = E + \dfrac{4\pi}{3}\, I, \end{array} \right\} \qquad [85]$$

where F is the force acting on a molecule within the element.   The
force F gives rise to an electric moment which is

$$m = \alpha_0 F + \mu L\left(\frac{\mu F}{kT} \right),$$

so that the polarization of the element is expressed by

$$I = nm = n\left[\alpha_0 F + \mu L\left(\frac{\mu F}{kT} \right) \right]. \qquad [85']$$

By means of equation $[85']$ I can be eliminated from $[85]$, giving

$$\left. \begin{array}{l} D - F = \dfrac{8\pi}{3}\left[n\alpha_0 F + n\mu L\left(\dfrac{\mu F}{kT} \right) \right], \\[4mm] E - F = -\dfrac{4\pi}{3}\left[n\alpha_0 F + n\mu L\left(\dfrac{\mu F}{kT} \right) \right]. \end{array} \right\} \qquad [86]$$

The explicit representation of D as a function of E requires the
elimination of F from these equations.   The best way to perform
this elimination is by a graphical method.   We may regard F in
$[86]$ as a parameter and plot D as well as E as a function of this
parameter.   Corresponding values of D and E can then be read at
once in the figure.   But as D is the dielectric displacement, it can
be calculated for any distance r from the charge by the formula

$$D = \frac{e}{r^2}. \qquad [86']$$

The figure will therefore give us corresponding values of r, E and D
for any abscissa F.

   Now let us take up the case where a small external field is superposed on the field of the ion, and ask how the dielectric constant
depends upon the direction in which it is measured.   The dielectric
constant measured along a line joining the element in question and

the ion (*i.e.* a radial line) is

$$\epsilon_r = \frac{dD}{dE} = \frac{dD}{dF} \Big/ \frac{dE}{dF}, \qquad [87]$$

but the two differential coefficients entering in this expression can be calculated from [86] in the form

$$\left.\begin{aligned} \frac{dD}{dF} &= 1 + \frac{8\pi}{3}\left[n\alpha_0 + \frac{n\mu^2}{kT} L'\left(\frac{\mu F}{kT}\right)\right], \\ \frac{dE}{dF} &= 1 - \frac{4\pi}{3}\left[n\alpha_0 + \frac{n\mu^2}{kT} L'\left(\frac{\mu F}{kT}\right)\right], \end{aligned}\right\} \qquad [87']$$

We found that by assuming any value of F the two quantities E and D and at the same time the distance r were given. Now we can calculate the two differential coefficients in [87'] for the same value of F and determine their quotient ϵ_r. We have then found the value of the radial dielectric constant for any distance r. If we apply in the element a small field of magnitude δE perpendicular to the radial direction, its effect is the same as if we had turned the field intensity E by an angle $\delta\theta$ given by the equation

$$\delta\theta = \frac{\delta E}{E}.$$

As a result the polarization and the dielectric displacement will turn by the same angle and we can say that to the vector D a vector of magnitude

$$\delta D = D\delta\theta = \frac{D}{E}\delta E$$

has been added, having the direction perpendicular to the radius. This, however, amounts to saying that the tangential dielectric constant ϵ_θ (*i.e.*, the dielectric constant for a small field applied perpendicular to r) will be

$$\epsilon_\theta = \frac{D}{E}. \qquad [87'']$$

As D and E are both known for every value of r, the tangential dielectric constant ϵ_θ also is known.

Figure 30 gives ϵ_r and ϵ_θ for water as a function of the distance from a monovalent ion, expressed in Angström units (10^{-8} cm.), assuming the optical dielectric constant to be 3 and the statical dielectric constant 80.

We are now prepared to treat the question as to how a small homogeneous field will be disturbed if we insert a center around which the dielectric constant behaves as shown by Figure 31.

This is the question which has to be treated to find the apparent dielectric constant of the solution. In general the equation

$$\text{div } D = 0$$

must be satisfied everywhere outside the ion. If now we call D_0 the displacement before applying the external field and δD the

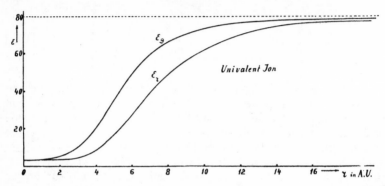

FIG. 30.   Saturation effect near an ion.

(vectorial) change in D_0 due to the superposed field, we must have

$$\text{div } \delta D = 0.$$

Expressing this equation in spherical coordinates and introducing the two components of δD in the direction of r and in a direction θ perpendicular to r, we obtain [11]

$$\frac{1}{r^2} \frac{\partial}{\partial r} (r^2 \delta D_r) + \frac{1}{r \sin \theta} (\sin \theta \delta D_\theta) = 0.$$

But we know that

$$\delta D_r = \epsilon_r \delta E_r,$$
$$\delta D_\theta = \epsilon_\theta \delta E_\theta,$$

and, as E always can be derived from a potential, we know further that

$$\delta E_r = -\frac{\partial \psi}{\partial r},$$
$$\delta E_\theta = -\frac{1}{r} \frac{\partial \psi}{\partial \theta}.$$

Using these relations, our differential equation becomes

$$\frac{\partial}{\partial r} \left(\epsilon_r r^2 \frac{\partial \psi}{\partial r} \right) + \frac{1}{\sin \theta} \frac{\partial}{\partial \theta} \left(\epsilon_\theta \sin \theta \frac{\partial \psi}{\partial \theta} \right) = 0. \qquad [88]$$

[11] The angle θ is measured between r and the direction of the superposed homogeneous field.

We require a solution of this equation which is regular at infinity and satisfies the boundary conditions at the surface of the ion.

In this differential equation ϵ_r and ϵ_θ are the complicated functions of r shown by Figure 31 and defined by [87] and [87'']. For large values of r the solution must approximate the function

$$\left(- Ar + \frac{B}{r^2} \right) \cos \theta,$$

where the constant B has the physical significance of being proportional to the apparent moment of the ion. Let us now try a solution of the form

$$\psi = R(r) \cos \theta.$$

Substituting this function in the differential equation, there results

$$\frac{d}{dr}\left[\epsilon_r r^2 \frac{dR}{dr} \right] - 2\epsilon_\theta R = 0. \qquad [89]$$

Being guided by the known form of the solution where r is large, we may write

$$R = - Af(r) + Bg(r), \qquad [90]$$

where

$$\lim_{r=\infty} \begin{cases} f(r) = r, \\ g(r) = \dfrac{1}{r^2} \end{cases}$$

and A is equal to the intensity X of the superposed field. We cannot obtain the solution for small values of r by solving the differential equation directly on account of the complicated form of ϵ_r and ϵ_θ. Sack obtained an approximate solution by means of a graphical method, starting with very large values of r and then obtaining solutions for successively smaller values by a method of approximations. With the help of the result of this graphical integration he derived finally

$$\epsilon^* = \epsilon(1 - 3c)$$

for a monovalent salt, the numerical factor 3 being practically independent of the size of the ion under ordinary conditions. By changing the assumptions made about the polarizability and the moment of the water molecule or in trying to take into account the association to some extent, the factor 3 will be changed appreciably, as Sack shows. For the salt KCl the experimental factor was 7; the only conclusion we can draw, therefore, is that a purely electrical calculation ultimately leads to a result which seems to be of the correct order of magnitude. The details of Sack's numerical calculation will not be given here; we will rather concern ourselves with the question as to what effect the magnitude of the ionic charge has upon the apparent dielectric constant. In order to evaluate the constant B, the boundary conditions at the surface of the ion must be considered. For this purpose we may liken the ion to a conducting sphere, which will simplify the boundary conditions. The choice of boundary conditions is practically arbitrary since, as Sack shows, the apparent dielectric constant depends materially only on the condition of the liquid in regions relatively remote from the ions. Although in these regions the change in dielectric constant is small, the volume occupied by these regions is so much larger than the regions near the ion that they give the principal part of the effect.

Remembering that ψ is the potential from which the superposed field has to be calculated, we have the boundary condition

$$\psi = 0 \qquad \text{or} \qquad R = 0, \qquad \text{for} \qquad r = a.$$

The constant A is equal to the field intensity X of the homogeneous field, so considering [90] we may therefore derive

$$B = X \frac{f(a)}{g(a)} . \qquad [91]$$

Now let us see how the value of B will be altered if we suppose the charge of the ion changed from e to ze. At a given distance r from the ion we will now have other values for ϵ_r and ϵ_θ, which we will call ϵ_r' and ϵ_θ'. But these new values are connected with the old ones in a very simple way. What we said about the calculation of ϵ_r and ϵ_θ shows that the new case differs from the old only in the calculation of the distance r. For we find first values of F, E, D, ϵ_r and ϵ_θ which belong together and afterwards we find the corresponding distance by applying now the formula

$$D = \frac{ze}{r^2}$$

and formerly the formula

$$D = \frac{e}{r^2}$$

If therefore ϵ_r and ϵ_θ can be represented in the first case by two formulas, such as

$$\epsilon_r = \Phi_1(r), \quad \epsilon_\theta = \Phi_2(r),$$

we will have in the case of the charge ze replacing e:

$$\epsilon_r' = \Phi_1\left(\frac{r}{\sqrt{z}}\right), \quad \epsilon_\theta' = \Phi_2\left(\frac{r}{\sqrt{z}}\right).$$

If we write for the potential in our second case

$$\psi' = R' \cos \theta,$$

the equation for R' is

$$\frac{d}{dr}\left(\epsilon_r' r^2 \frac{dR'}{dr}\right) - 2\epsilon_\theta' R' = 0.$$

But if we introduce the new variable $r' = r/\sqrt{z}$, this equation takes the same form as the original equation because ϵ_r' and ϵ_θ' are just the same functions of r' as ϵ_r and ϵ_θ are of r. That is why we will have

$$R' = - A'f\left(\frac{r}{\sqrt{z}}\right) + B'g\left(\frac{r}{\sqrt{z}}\right), \qquad [92]$$

giving in the limit for large values of r according to [90]

$$R' = - A'\frac{r}{\sqrt{z}} + B'\frac{z}{r^2}. \qquad [92']$$

The multiplier of r has to be equal to X and the boundary condition applied to [92] gives

$$B' = A'\frac{f\left(\dfrac{a}{\sqrt{z}}\right)}{g\left(\dfrac{a}{\sqrt{z}}\right)} = \sqrt{z}\,\frac{f\left(\dfrac{a}{\sqrt{z}}\right)}{g\left(\dfrac{a}{\sqrt{z}}\right)}X. \qquad [93]$$

Now we already mentioned that if for large distances the disturbance due to the ion is proportional to $(\cos\theta)/r^2$, the term multiplying this expression is proportional to the electric moment equivalent to the action of the ion with its surroundings. For the charge e this multiplier was, according to [91],

$$B = \frac{f(a)}{g(a)}X; \qquad [94]$$

for the charge ze it is, according to [92'] and [93],

$$B'z = z^{3/2}\frac{f\left(\dfrac{a}{\sqrt{z}}\right)}{g\left(\dfrac{a}{\sqrt{z}}\right)}X. \qquad [94']$$

As all induced electric moments are proportional to these factors the quotient of the right-hand sides of [94] and [94'] will be at the same time the quotient of the changes in dielectric constant created by ions of charge e and ze. In general it is impossible to infer the value of this quotient from [94] and [94'] without knowing the functions f and g. But in our case we know that the final result is practically independent of the size of the ion; that is, it does not matter if we choose the argument a or $a/\sqrt{z}$. This being so, then we have found the rule that the influence of an ion should be proportional to the 3/2 power of its valence. To express this result in a formula let us suppose that a salt has been dissolved consisting of

$$\nu_1 \cdots \nu_i \cdots \nu_s$$

ions of the valencies

$$z_1 \cdots z_i \cdots z_s;$$

the coefficient γ in [84] should then be proportional to

$$\sum_1^s \nu_i z_i^{3/2},$$

with a proportionality constant the same for all kinds of salts provided the radius of the ion is small enough compared with the range of the saturation-effect. Table XX contains a number of salts which have been measured by Sack.

TABLE XX. *The Influence of Valency.*

Salt	ν_i	z_i	γ experiment	error	γ calculated
KCl.........			6.9	±1.0	
NaCl........	$\nu_1 = 1, \nu_2 = 2$	$z_1 = 1, z_2 = 1$	7.1	±1.2	6.6
LiCl........			7.4	±1.4	
BaCl$_2$........	$\nu_1 = 1, \nu_2 = 2$	$z_1 = 2, z_2 = 1$	16.5	±2.8	15.8
MgSO$_4$......	$\nu_1 = 1, \nu_2 = 1$	$z_1 = 2, z_2 = 2$	17.3	±2.7	18.5
CuSO$_4$.......			19.0	±2.3	
La(NO$_3$)$_3$....	$\nu_1 = 1, \nu_2 = 3$	$z_1 = 3, z_2 = 1$	24.2	±3.4	27.1
LaCl$_3$.......			26.5	±3.5	

The experimental values of γ are given together with the presumable error. The calculated values of γ, in the last column, have been computed by the equation

$$\gamma = 3.3 \sum \nu_i z_i^{3/2}, \qquad [95]$$

wherein the factor 3.3 has been chosen to fit the experimental results. The table gives the impression that the valency law expressed by [95] might hold.

In concluding this chapter it should be emphasized that the whole subject of saturation in ionic solutions and connected phenomena has been treated in a highly hypothetical way. On the other hand the existing experiments are far from satisfactory. In Table XXI are given the results of measurements of the dielectric constants of aqueous solutions of electrolytes, which have appeared in recent

TABLE XXI. γ-Values of Various Salts.

Author	Method	Frequency	1;1			1;2		2;2		1;3		1;4		1;1		
			KCl	NaCl	SiCl	$BaCl_2$	$Ba(ClO_4)_2$	$CuSO_4$	$MgSO_4$	$LaCl_3$	$La(NO_3)_3$	$Th(NO_3)_4$	$K_4Fe(CN)_6$	HCl	KOH	NaOH
A. Deubner[1]	1st Drude	1.5×10^8	—	<0.06	—	—	—	7.2	—	—	—	—	—	—	—	—
B. Voigt[2]	2d Drude	0.7×10^9	0	—	—	—	—	—	—	—	—	—	—	—	—	—
P. Walden, H. Ulich[3] O. Werner	Resonance	0.7×10^8	20.2	21.0	20.4	45.0	35.3	35.6	17.3	—	68.2	100	98	58.5	26.5	—
H. Sack[4]	Bridge	2×10^6	6.9	7.1	7.4	16.5	—	19.0	—	26.5	24.2	—	—	—	—	—
R. Skaneke and E. Schreiner[5]	Bridge *	0.8×10^6	2.5	—	2.3	8.3	—	—	16.6	—	13.0	—	32.0	—	—	—
R. Pechhold[6]	Ellipsoid †	50	6.5(9)	14(21)	16(18)	—	—	—	—	—	—	—	—	(58)	—	(32)
H. Hellmann and H. Zahn[7]	Control experiments with different methods	3×10^8	0.7–2.2	—	—	—	—	—	—	—	—	—	—	—	—	—

[1] Ann. Physik, **84**, 429 (1927).
[2] Z. Physik, **44**, 70 (1927).
[3] Z. physik. Chem., **129**, 389 (1927) (see there more literature).
[4] Physik. Z., **28**, 199 (1927).
[5] Physik. Z., **28**, 597 (1927).
[6] Ann. Physik, **83**, 427 (1927).
[7] Physik. Z., **27**, 636 (1926).
* The numbers are taken from the paper of reference 7.
† The numbers in parentheses are estimated by Walden [3] and seem indeed to fit the experimental results better.

years (earlier experiments of Nernst, Drude, Sommer and others have been omitted. Likewise the results of Hellmann and Zahn [12] obtained by the so-called decrement method are not included. They are only exact for high concentrations and there only for relative values and it is quite impossible to extrapolate with any degree of accuracy to such small concentrations as have been used by the authors noted in the table). In the first column are given the names of the authors; in the second the methods used, and in the third the frequencies of the electric oscillations. The first and second methods of Drude as well as the Nernst-Bridge method (designed in the Table by "Bridge") have been used for many years in measuring dielectric constants. The resonance method (measurement of capacity by resonating circuit) and the ellipsoid method (twisting force on an ellipsoid of metal) have been devised especially for the dielectric constants of conducting media. The control experiments of Hellmann and Zahn have been carried out with the Drude and Resonance methods, but give only the magnitude of the value γ.

In the following columns are noted the γ-values for the different salts. They are arranged according to their valency, which is given at the head of the table. We segregate HCl, KOH and NaOH, as it is doubtful whether the theory can be applied to such ions as H and OH. The table shows clearly the big differences, even in magnitude, of the different experimenters. It may be interesting to state that the authors who find for mono-monovalent salts no influence ($\gamma \sim 0$) give a rather high γ-value for $CuSO_4$. The valency relation is satisfied most completely by the values of Sack, less completely by those of Skancke and Schreiner and of Walden and his collaborators, and not at all by those of Deubner. It is doubtful whether these differences can be explained by the differences in frequency. The fact is that no definite conclusions with regard to any theory can be drawn from the measurements in their present condition. Old methods will have to be improved and new methods introduced. But I did not like to eliminate this chapter altogether, because I hope that it may give an impulse towards further experimental and theoretical activity in this field.

[12] *Physik. Z.*, **28**, 916 (1927); *Ann. Physik*, **81**, 711 (1926).

CHAPTER VII

DIELECTRIC PHENOMENA AND QUANTUM THEORY

24. The Thermodynamic Potential and the Quantum States.

We shall now depart from our study of special systems and consider the broader question as to the meaning of our most general results, in terms of the quantum theory. In general we have found that when a system of molecules or atoms is placed in an electric field F the mean molecular or atomic moment is related to the field strength by an equation of the form

$$m = \left(a + \frac{b}{T} \right)F.$$

If this is indeed a general law, the constants a and b should have a meaning in terms of the energy levels introduced in quantum theory. From now on we will assume that every system to be considered can occur in a certain number of quantum states each of definite energy. It is characteristic for the formula that the temperature is of importance. Therefore we will have to deal with the thermodynamic properties of the system and this we propose to do starting with Boltzmann's hypothesis concerning the connection between entropy and probability.

Suppose there exist different quantum states i of energy levels w_i over which a number of systems Z may be distributed. The number of systems in the state i may be designated by z_i. In general these possible quantum states will not all have the same a priori probability ρ_i. If we calculate the probability p of a certain distribution characterized by the numbers

$$z_1 \cdots z_i \cdots$$

we find in the usual way

$$p = Z!\Pi\left(\frac{\rho_i{}^{z_i}}{z_i!} \right), \tag{96}$$

where the sign Π has the meaning "Product."

The probability of the distribution $z_1 \ldots z_i$ for Z definite systems, each of which is supposed to have a special characterization such that it can be distinguished from all others, is

$$\Pi(\rho_i{}^{z_i}).$$

But if the distribution is considered as defined by the number of systems in each state only and one system cannot be distinguished from another, this product has to be multiplied with

$$\frac{z!}{\Pi(z_i!)};$$

for this is the number of possible interchanges keeping the values $z_1, \ldots z_i, \ldots$ each constant. The simplest representation of p is that given by Laplace in his "Théorie des probabilités" as the term containing the factor

$$\rho_1{}^{z_1}\rho_2{}^{z_2} \ldots \rho^{z_i} \ldots$$

in the development of

$$(\rho_1 + \rho_2 + \ldots + \rho + \ldots)^{Z=z_1+z_2+\cdots+z_i+\cdots}.$$

If the *a priori* probabilities are chosen such that $\Sigma\rho_i = 1$, the quantity p is a probability of the usual definition in statistics.

The probability p will be a maximum under the supplementary conditions that the total number of systems

$$Z = \sum z_i$$

and the total energy

$$W = \sum z_i w_i$$

is kept constant, in which case

$$z_i = z_i = \alpha\rho_i e^{-\beta w_i}, \tag{97}$$

where α and β are two constants defined by the equations

$$\left.\begin{array}{l} Z = \alpha\sum\rho_i e^{-\beta w_i}, \\ W = \alpha\sum\rho_i w_i e^{-\beta w_i}. \end{array}\right\} \tag{98}$$

This result may be obtained in the usual way, applying Stirling's formula for the factorial

$$n! = \sqrt{2\pi n}\left(\frac{n}{e}\right)^u$$

to [96], calculating log p, and considering every z_i as large enough that Stirling's formula may be applied. As the laws of pure thermodynamics have to be considered as the limiting laws for lim $Z = \infty$, there is no objection against this application.[1]

As one system under consideration we will in general take not one mólecule, but the body with which the experiment is done, such that every interaction of the individual molecules is included and all the molecules together build the system of which the different quantum states of energy w_i are considered. If such a system has the internal energy U and the electric moment M in a field of intensity E, its average energy is

$$U - ME$$

according to the ordinary definition of U and M, disregarding the

[1] *Compare* P. Debye, *Ann. Physik*, (4) **33**, 441 (1910).

fluctuation of these quantities.   We will therefore let

$$W = Z(U - ME).$$ [98']

We can introduce the value $z_i = \bar{z}_i$ of [97] in our expression [96] for p and calculate the value

$$p = \bar{p}$$

corresponding to this special distribution.   Following Boltzmann the thermodynamic entropy is then equal to $k \log \bar{p}$, where $k = 1.37 \times 10^{-16}$ ergs is Boltzmann's constant.   We will represent the entropy of Z systems by ZS in the same way as we introduced the internal energy as ZU, giving

$$ZS = k \log \bar{p}.$$ [99]

Introducing Stirling's formula in [96], this equation will give

$$\frac{1}{k} ZS = Z \log Z + \sum \bar{z}_i \log \rho_i - \sum \bar{z}_i \log \bar{z}_i,$$

but this expression can easily be reduced to

$$\frac{S}{k} = \log Z - \log \alpha + \beta \frac{W}{Z},$$ [100]

as $\bar{z}_i$ is represented by equation [97].   Let us denote by σ the sum

$$\sigma = \sum \rho_i e^{-\beta w_i}$$ [101]

This sum will play an important part in subsequent calculations; we will call it the "sum of state" and express our result with its aid.   If we differentiate σ with respect to β, keeping the parameters which are included in w_i constant, and call this differential coefficient σ', it is seen that, taking account of [98'], equations [98] can be put in the form

$$\left. \begin{array}{l} \alpha = \dfrac{Z}{\sigma}, \\[2mm] \dfrac{W}{Z} = U - ME = -\dfrac{\sigma'}{\sigma}. \end{array} \right\}$$ [102]

Therefore we derive from [100] another expression for the entropy, namely,

$$\frac{S}{k} = \log \sigma - \beta \frac{\sigma'}{\sigma}.$$ [100']

From a theoretical point of view we have now finished.   For suppose

we have calculated the sum of state [101] as a function of β.   With
the help of the second equation of [102] it will then be possible to
calculate β as a function of $U - ME$ and, applying [100'], the
entropy will be expressed in the ordinary variable used in thermodynamic calculations.   This process would involve the rather
cumbersome calculation of β by the second equation of [102].   It
is of some practical importance to see how this can be avoided.
With this aim in mind, we will prove first that β is very simply
connected with the absolute temperature.   If in equation [100']
we change β to $\beta + d\beta$ and call the corresponding change of the
entropy dS, we find

$$dS = - k\beta d\left(\frac{\sigma'}{\sigma}\right).$$

But by the second equation of [102] we also have

$$- d\left(\frac{\sigma'}{\sigma}\right) = dU - EdM,$$

because while we changed β the other implicit variables, in particular
the field intensity E, were kept constant.   This is made evident in
the definition of σ', which involves a process in which w_i, which
will contain E as a parameter, was not taken to be changed.   We
therefore have finally

$$dS = k\beta(dU - EdM). \tag{103}$$

Now according to the first law of thermodynamics the change in
energy dU is equal to the amount of heat δQ plus the amount of
work δA put into the system.   In our case, the work is electrical
and equal [2] to EdM, and dU can be expressed in the form

$$dU = \delta Q + EdM.$$

The second law of thermodynamics states that

$$dS = \frac{\delta Q}{T}$$

and from these two equations compared with [103] it is evident that

$$\beta = \frac{1}{kT}. \tag{104}$$

Introducing this value of β in [101] gives us for the sum of state
the expression

$$\sigma = \sum \rho_i e^{-(w_i/kT)} \tag{105}$$

and by this equation σ is now known as a function of T and the

[2] *Compare* P. Debye, "Handbuch d. Radiologie," **VI**, p. 742.

parameters contained in w_i, of which in our case the field intensity E is most important. Remembering the second equation of [102], the expression [100'] can be rearranged in the form

$$\Phi = U - TS - ME = - kT \log \sigma. \qquad [106]$$

The combination $U - TS - ME$, designated by Φ, is a thermodynamic potential according to the ordinary definition. The appropriate variables are T and E. For if we change only these two we can derive

$$d\Phi = - SdT - MdE$$

with the aid of the equation expressing dU in the form

$$dU = \delta Q + EdM = TdS + EdM.$$

In other words we will find the electric moment M of our system in calculating

$$M = - \frac{\partial \Phi}{\partial E}, \qquad [107]$$

provided Φ is expressed as a function of T and E. But this is really performed by equation [106], for the sum of state contains only T and, included in w_i, the field intensity E as parameters. The only thing we have to do, if the quantum states are known, is then to calculate the sum of state by [105]. Equation [106] will then give the thermodynamic potential and the electric moment will follow by the differentiation indicated in [107].[3]

25. The Dielectric Constant and the Stark Effect.

Let us suppose that we are dealing with molecules which are so far apart that their interaction may be neglected. It is then perfectly possible to speak of the thermodynamic potential Φ of one molecule in temperature equilibrium with its surroundings. This potential will be defined by [106] together with the sum of state entering in this definition through [105]. The *a priori* probability ρ_i and the energy w_i refer now to the different possible quantum levels of the molecule, and the average electric moment m will be given by [107]. A system consisting of N such molecules will have a thermodynamic potential N times as large as the potential calculated for one particle and there is no need of making a distinction between the electric intensity E and the internal field F.

If we are to speak of a dielectric *constant* of such a system, the average moment m has to be proportional to E, or in other words if the thermodynamic potential is expanded in powers of E no higher powers than E^2 have to be considered.

[3] *Compare* P. Debye, *Physik. Z.*, **27**, 67 (1926).

If the molecule is not under the influence of an external field, it will be characterized by the existence of a number of energy levels of energy w_i. Applying the field E, these levels will be shifted and sometimes split into different levels. This can be the case if the original level had already a multiplicity larger than 1, i.e., if it really consisted of a superposition of more than one level, which happened to have the same energy. To avoid introducing explicitly the multiplicity in our formula, we will consider every level of multiplicity s as a superposition of s independent levels all with the same energy. After this definition of a single quantum state, we have to introduce a hypothesis about the value of the a priori probability of such a state. We will assume that the a priori probability of all single states is the same irrespective of their energy content. This hypothesis recalls Boltzmann's hypothesis giving the same a priori probability to elements of volume in the phase-space having the same size, i.e., assuming that for a system characterized by the coordinates $q_1 \cdots q_n$ and the corresponding momenta $p_1 \cdots p_n$ the a priori probability is proportional to

$$dq_1 \cdots dq_{n}, \ dp_1 \cdots dp_n$$

with the factor 1, independent of the coordinates $q_1 \cdots q_n$, $p_1 \cdots p_n$. To avoid an unnecessary factor we will assume every a priori probability $\rho_i = 1$.

Let us now apply the field E; the energy of every level will then be changed and we will assume that this energy can be expressed in the form

$$w_i = w_i^* - \mu_i E - \frac{\alpha_i}{2} E^2, \qquad [108]$$

μ_i and α_i being constants characteristic of the level in question. In other words we assume that every level will be shifted in the way characteristic for the Stark effect and we will see that the linear as well as the quadratic part of it has to be considered. The quantity μ_i has the dimension of an electric moment and α_i of a polarizability, that is, of a volume. In fact the electrical part of the energy can be visualized as the energy of a particle which has a permanent moment μ_i, set parallel to the field, and a polarizability α_i. Higher powers of E in the expression for w_i need not be considered, as we are only interested now in the part of the average moment which is linear in the field intensity. The only thing we have to do is carrying out the process of calculation described at the end of Section 24. The sum of state is given by [105] and from what has been said about ρ_i and the definition of a single state we have

$$\sigma = \sum e^{-(w_i^*/kT)} e^{(1/kT)[\mu_i E + (\alpha_i/2)E^2]}.$$

If the right-hand member is developed in powers of E, there results

$$\sigma = \sum e^{-(w_i*/kT)} + \frac{E}{kT} \sum \mu_i e^{-(w_i*/kT)}$$
$$+ \frac{E^2}{2kT} \left\{ \sum \alpha_i e^{-(w_i/kT)} + \frac{1}{kT} \sum \mu_i{}^2 e^{-(w_i/kT)} \right\}.$$

For convenience of notation, we will introduce

$$\left. \begin{aligned} \sigma_0 &= \sum e^{-(w_i*/kT)}, \\ \sigma_1 &= \sum \mu_i e^{-(w_i*/kT)}, \\ \sigma_2' &= \sum \alpha_i e^{-(w_i*/kT)}, \\ \sigma_2'' &= \sum \mu_i{}^2 e^{-(w_i*/kT)}. \end{aligned} \right\} \qquad [109]$$

Using this notation, we have

$$\sigma = \sigma_0 + \frac{E}{kT} \sigma_1 + \frac{E^2}{2kT} \sigma_2 \qquad [110]$$

where

$$\sigma_2 = \sigma_2' + \frac{1}{kT} \sigma_2''. \qquad [110']$$

The second step is the calculation of $\log \sigma$ expanded in the same way in powers of E.   It is found that

$$\log \sigma = \log \sigma_0 + \frac{E}{kT} \frac{\sigma_1}{\sigma_0} + \frac{E^2}{2kT} \left\{ \frac{\sigma_2}{\sigma_0} - \left(\frac{\sigma_1}{\sigma_0} \right)^2 \right\}$$

and equation [106] gives for the thermodynamic potential Φ the expression

$$\Phi = - kT \log \sigma_0 - E \frac{\sigma_1}{\sigma_0} - \frac{E^2}{2} \left\{ \frac{\sigma_2}{\sigma_0} - \left(\frac{\sigma_1}{\sigma_0} \right)^2 \right\}. \qquad [111]$$

Finally, the average electric moment m is calculated by the differentiation indicated in [107], giving

$$m = \frac{\sigma_1}{\sigma_0} + \left\{ \frac{\sigma_2}{\sigma_0} - \left(\frac{\sigma_1}{\sigma_0} \right)^2 \right\} E. \qquad [112]$$

In all the cases which we will have to consider hereafter no average electric moment exists unless a field E is present.   In this case $\sigma_1/\sigma_0 = 0$ and we have simply

$$m = \frac{\sigma_2}{\sigma_0} E = \left(\frac{\sigma_2'}{\sigma_0} + \frac{1}{kT} \frac{\sigma_2''}{\sigma_0} \right) E, \qquad [112']$$

taking account of [110']. In general the sums σ_0, σ_2' and σ_2'' are functions of the temperature, and the coefficient of E will by no means be a linear function of $1/T$. The part which follows will make clear, however, that in the cases with which we will be concerned it practically reduces to such a linear function.[4] One very simple case exists for which the coefficient is linear in $1/T$. If, namely, the energy difference between the first level and all the following levels is large compared with kT, it is only necessary to take account of the first term in calculating the sums and it is found

$$m = \left(\alpha_1 + \frac{\mu_1{}^2}{kT} \right) E.$$

Further progress can be made in actually calculating the energy levels. This will be done in the next chapter.

[4] An excellent general survey is given by J. H. van Vleck, *Phys. Rev.*, **29** 727 (1927); **30**, 31 (1927).

CHAPTER VIII

ENERGY LEVELS AND WAVE MECHANICS

26. Geometrical Optics and Classical Mechanics. In the previous treatment of the behavior of the dielectric constant in terms of quantum theory the existence of definite energy levels was assumed. The remaining question is as to how these energy levels can be calculated if we believe the constitution of the molecular system to be known. In the quantum theory as developed by Bohr and others, these levels were found by calculating the motion of the system with the help of classical mechanics and separating out those motions for which certain characteristic phase integrals are equal to a whole number times Planck's quantum of action h. The energy of these so-called stationary motions was considered as the energy of the different levels. The more modern quantum theory started by Heisenberg, brought to a general, mathematically possible form by Born and Jordan, and in another possible form by Schrödinger, who built up on considerations first imagined by de Broglie, tries to establish a much closer connection between the molecule and a certain corresponding vibrational system. We will prefer Schrödinger's treatment, which culminates in the substitution for classical mechanics of its generalization called wave mechanics and enables us to have a mental picture throughout.

The connection between wave mechanics and classical mechanics is in close analogy to the connection existing between wave optics and geometrical optics. It is starting from this standpoint that we will give a review of the principles involved and their application to our special problems.

The first step is to show how geometrical optics can be derived as the limiting case for small wave-lengths, or high frequencies, from the partial differential equation describing the field in wave optics. If considered purely by itself it has nothing to do with quantum theory.[1] Suppose we are dealing with a medium in which the velocity of light v is a function of the coordinates. The propagation of light can then be described by the wave equation

$$\nabla^2 \Psi - \frac{1}{v^2} \frac{\partial^2 \Psi}{\partial t^2} = 0,$$

[1] Compare a remark of P. Debye on p. 240 in A. Sommerfeld and J. Runge, *Ann. Physik*, **35**, 277 (1911). The connections with quantum theory are treated by G. Wentzel, *Z. Physik*, **37**, 80 (1926); L. Brillouin, *Compt. rend.*, **183**, 24 (1926); L. de Broglie, *J. phys.*, (6) **7**, 321 (1926); H. A. Kramers, *Z. Physik*, **39**, 828 (1926); P. Debye, *Physik. Z.*, **28**, 170 (1927).

in which Ψ may be taken as representing for instance a component of the electric intensity. We wish to investigate the laws of propagation of a disturbance of very high frequency, expecting that in the limit, for infinite frequency and correspondingly infinitely small wave-length, we will arrive at the laws of geometrical optics. We introduce

$$\Psi = \psi e^{-i\omega t} \qquad [113]$$

and have for the quantity ψ the equation

$$\nabla^2 \psi - \left(\frac{i\omega}{v}\right)^2 \psi = 0. \qquad [114]$$

To arrive at a solution of this equation, which will hold for very large values of the coefficient of ψ, we introduce a new function V of the coordinates by the substitution

$$\psi = e^{i\omega V}. \qquad [115]$$

We are guided by the fact that in geometrical optics Ψ would be represented by a function of the form

$$\Psi = A(x, y, z)e^{i\omega[f(x, y, z)-t]},$$

in which the surfaces $f(x, y, z) = $ const. would represent the surfaces of constant phase. Introducing [115] in [114] gives the equation

$$\text{grad}^2 V + \frac{1}{i\omega} \nabla^2 V = \frac{1}{v^2}. \qquad [116]$$

Now remembering that we are interested in the solution for very large values of ω, we try the series

$$V = V_0 + \frac{1}{i\omega} V_1 + \frac{1}{(i\omega)^2} V_2 + \cdots, \qquad [117]$$

developing V according to ascending powers of the small quantity $1/\omega$. Substituting [117] in [116] and comparing the coefficients of every power of $1/i\omega$ on both sides, we obtain the following series of equations:

$$\left.\begin{array}{l} \text{grad}^2 V_0 = \dfrac{1}{v^2}, \\[2mm] 2\,(\text{grad}\, V_0 \times \text{grad}\, V_1) + \nabla^2 V_0 = 0, \\[2mm] \cdot\ \cdot\ \cdot\ \cdot\ \cdot\ \cdot\ \cdot\ \cdot\ \cdot\ \cdot\ \cdot\ \cdot\ \cdot \end{array}\right\} \qquad [118]$$

which will enable us to calculate successively V_0, V_1, etc. In the limit for $\omega = \infty$ we have to know only the first two of these functions V_0 and V_1, for if we introduce the series [117] in [115], we see that in the limit ψ will be represented by

$$\psi = e^{V_1} e^{i\omega V_0}. \qquad [119]$$

The function V_0 will therefore define the surface of constant phase, whereas V_1 will define the amplitude of the vibrations. The two equations [118] represent together the ordinary laws used to characterize the rays and their intensities in geometrical optics. This can be seen in the following way.

Suppose we have chosen an arbitrary surface on which V_0 is taken to be constant, say equal to C. The first equation of [118] will tell us how we can construct the next surface on which V_0 will be equal to another constant $C + \delta C$, larger than C by an infinitely small amount δC. For calling δn a small length perpendicular to the surface, the equation can be written

$$\frac{\delta V_0}{\delta n} = \pm \frac{1}{v}, \qquad [120]$$

since the gradient in any direction lying in the surface itself is zero. Either the positive or the negative sign can be taken but we will only consider the positive sign, because changing the sign merely means reversing the direction of propagation. Now $\delta V_0 = \delta C$ and therefore the equation means that we have to erect normals of the lengths

$$\delta n = v \delta C \qquad [121]$$

in every point of the surface $V_0 = C$ to arrive at the next surface $V_0 = C + \delta C$. As v is a function of the coordinates, the normals will differ in length at different points.

It is evident from [113] and [119] that

$$V_0 - t = \text{const.} = K$$

defines a surface on which the phase is constant. We can ask, what is the velocity with which this surface travels? Draw normals δn to the surface $V_0 = C$ and give them the length

$$\delta n = q \delta t; \qquad [121']$$

if then q is chosen such that the ends of these normals define a surface on which $V_0 - (t + \delta t)$ is equal to the same value K as before, we will have to call q the velocity of propagation (or better, the phase-velocity). Now take $q = v$ and $\delta t = \delta C$, so that according to [121'] and [121] we will then have reached a surface on which everywhere V_0 has changed by δC. But t having changed by δt, therefore $V_0 - t$ has not changed at all. We can now say that the quantity v of our original equation may properly be called the phase velocity. As the rays of light we can take the normal trajectories of our set of surfaces $V_0 = C$, of which every one can be developed from a first one, which is itself arbitrary.

The second equation tells us about the change in amplitude going from one surface to the next. Suppose we spread arbitrary values of V_1 over the surface $V_0 = C$. There will then exist a grad V_1 in the surface itself. The equation leaves this gradient absolutely indeterminate and we can choose for V_1 on the surface any function we like. Calling the normal again δn, we can write the second equation of [118] in the form

$$\frac{\delta V_0}{\delta n} \frac{\delta V_1}{\delta n} = -\frac{1}{2} \operatorname{div} \operatorname{grad} V_0, \qquad [122]$$

because no grad V_0 in the direction of the surface exists. Now let us consider a bundle of rays with the small cross-section s; the right-hand part of the foregoing equation can then be calculated as

$$-\frac{1}{2} \frac{\delta\left(s\frac{\delta V_0}{\delta n}\right)}{s\delta n}$$

by the ordinary geometrical definition of divergence. On the other hand we found by equation [120]

$$\frac{\delta V_0}{\delta n} = \frac{1}{v};$$

introducing this in [122] brings it to the form

$$\delta V_1 = -\frac{1}{2} \frac{\delta\left(\dfrac{s}{v}\right)}{\dfrac{s}{v}}. \qquad [122']$$

Going along one ray of the bundle, we can integrate [122'] and find

$$V_1 = \log \frac{\text{const.}}{\sqrt{\dfrac{s}{v}}}. \qquad [122'']$$

Now e^{V_1} was what we had to call the amplitude $A(x, y, z)$ and we see that along one bundle of rays

$$A = \text{const.} \sqrt{\frac{v}{s}}. \qquad [123]$$

If we take for instance the special case $v = \text{const.}$, equation [123] expresses the familiar fact in geometrical optics that in a bundle of rays the product of the square of A with the cross-section remains constant. That is why in geometrical optics we take the intensity proportional to the square of the amplitude.

Having thus seen how the rules of geometrical optics are included in the equations [118], we will next recall how the motion of a particle of mass m, moving in a field with the potential energy function $U(x, y, z)$, can be represented. If in classical mechanics the system under consideration can be characterized by n general coordinates $q_1 \cdots q_n$ and the n corresponding momenta $p_1 \cdots p_n$, and if we call the sum of kinetic and potential energy expressed in these two n variables the Hamiltonian function H, the motion of the system can be determined by solving the partial differential equation

$$\frac{\partial S}{\partial t} + H\left(q_1 \cdots q_n, \quad p_1 = \frac{\partial S}{\partial q_1} \cdots p_n = \frac{\partial S}{\partial q_n} \right) = 0. \qquad [124]$$

This equation is built with the help of the Hamiltonian function H in replacing formally in this function every momentum by the partial differential coefficient of S with respect to the corresponding coordinate. If a solution S of this equation is found as a function of the time t and the coordinates $q_1 \cdots q_n$, containing n mutually independent arbitrary constants $\alpha_1 \cdots \alpha_n$, the coordinates are expressed as functions of the time by the equations

$$\left.\begin{aligned} \beta_1 &= \frac{\partial S}{\partial \alpha_1}, \\ \cdot & \quad \cdot \\ \cdot & \quad \cdot \\ \cdot & \quad \cdot \\ \beta_n &= \frac{\partial S}{\partial \alpha_n}, \end{aligned}\right\} \qquad [125]$$

in which $\beta_1 \cdots \beta_n$ are a second set of n arbitrary constants. The n momenta $p_1 \cdots p_n$ can be found by differentiating S with respect to the n coordinates

$$\left.\begin{aligned} p_1 &= \frac{\partial S}{\partial q_1}, \\ \cdot & \quad \cdot \\ \cdot & \quad \cdot \\ \cdot & \quad \cdot \\ p_n &= \frac{\partial S}{\partial q_n}. \end{aligned}\right\} \qquad [126]$$

The two arbitrary sets of constants $\alpha_1 \cdots \beta_n$ can serve to introduce the n coordinates and the n momenta with which the system is supposed to start. In the special case of a particle of mass m moving in ordinary space in a field of potential energy U the fundamental equation takes the form

$$\frac{\partial S}{\partial t} + \frac{1}{2m}\,\text{grad}^2\,S + U = 0, \qquad [127]$$

for the total energy is

$$H = \frac{1}{2m}\,(\xi^2 + \eta^2 + \zeta^2) + U(x, y, z)$$

if ξ, η, ζ are the momenta (mass times component of the velocity) corresponding to the rectangular coordinates x, y, z, defining the location of the particle. In this case the Hamiltonian function does not contain the time explicitly, and we can therefore introduce a characteristic function V_m dependent only on the coordinates, using the substitution:

$$S = V_m(x, y, z) - Wt. \qquad [128]$$

As is seen from [124] the constant W has the meaning of the total energy, which is constant throughout the motion. The characteristic function V_m has to be a solution of the equation [2]

$$\text{grad}^2\,V_m = 2m(W - U). \qquad [129]$$

Let us now compare equation [129] with the first equation of [118] characteristic for the propagation of light in geometrical optics. It is seen at once that a close connection exists between the rays in optics and the path of a particle in classical mechanics. If we call the vectorial momentum of the particle **p**, the equations [126] express that **p** can be found in calculating

$$\mathbf{p} = \text{grad}\,V_m.$$

Now the vector **p** gives the direction of the path of the particle whereas in optics grad V_0 gave the direction of the ray. Without going into further detail it is sufficient for our purpose to note that whereas the rays in optics are the normal trajectories of a set of surfaces characterized by the first equation of [118], the possible paths of a particle are the normal trajectories of a set of surfaces, which are defined by the exactly similar equation [129].

[2] We confine our attention to the simple case of three coordinates. It is possible to generalize the results and to give the corresponding geometrical interpretation for any number of coordinates.

27. Wave Optics and Wave Mechanics.

The close relation between ray optics and classical mechanics applied to the movement of a particle, discussed in the foregoing Section 26, bears on the resemblance of the geometrical form of the ray and the path. At first sight there seems to be nothing in classical mechanics which can be compared with the frequency in optics. Since Bohr's explanation of the spectrum of the hydrogen atom, however, we are accustomed to connect the frequency ν of an optical phenomenon with the energy difference ΔW, involved in the process of emission, by the equation

$$\Delta W = h\nu$$

(h = Planck's quantum of action = 6.55×10^{-27}). It was de Broglie [3] who worked out the idea of constructing for a mechanical system a corresponding vibrating system and giving this a frequency defined by its total energy W, according to the equation

$$W = h\nu;$$

which can be interpreted as a generalization of Bohr's principle. If then the mechanical motion is characterized by the function

$$S = V_m - Wt, \qquad [130]$$

where V_m is defined by the Hamiltonian equation [129], it seems probable that the wave motion in the corresponding system should be described by a wave function

$$\Psi = A e^{i(2\pi/h)S} = A e^{i(2\pi/h)(V_m - Wt)}. \qquad [131]$$

In this way the frequency is as it should be W/h and the surfaces of constant phase are known, for V_m is supposed to be the function defined by Hamilton's equation [129]. The equation [131] contains the amplitude A, which will be a function of the coordinates also; but in classical mechanics nothing seems to be contained which leads to a definition of A. This attitude will be changed, however, as soon as we remember that to characterize geometrical optics we needed the two equations [118], of which only the first corresponded to an equation in classical mechanics. It would be perfectly possible to introduce the supposition that the amplitude has to be defined by an equation of the kind of the second equation [118]. In this way the vibrations in the corresponding system would be known in the sense of geometrical optics.

But we know that the laws of geometrical optics are only an approximation. It seems therefore reasonable that we should not content ourselves with the two equations [118], which after all are

[3] L. de Broglie, *Ann. Physik*, **3**, 22 (1925); "Ondes et Mouvements," Paris, Gauthier-Villars, 1926.

only the first two of an infinite set, but go back to the original wave equation [114] from which this set has been derived. This is Schrödinger's idea, which can be expressed in the following way.[4] The wave equation [114] has the form

$$\nabla^2 \psi - \left(\frac{i\omega}{v}\right)^2 \psi = 0$$

and it has been settled that

$$\omega = 2\pi \frac{W}{h}.$$

The phase velocity v remains to be determined. From [115] and [117] it is clear that we will have

$$\psi = A e^{i(2\pi/h)WV_0}$$

if V_0 is defined by the first equation of [118], i.e.,

$$\text{grad}^2 V_0 = \frac{1}{v^2}.$$

On the other hand [131] shows that

$$\psi = A e^{i(2\pi/h)V_m}$$

and V_m is defined by the Hamiltonian equation [129], i.e.,

$$\text{grad}^2 V_m = 2m(W - U).$$

Therefore if a correspondence has to exist for high frequencies, or better in the limit for $h = 0$, the quantity $W \times V_0$ should be compared with V_m; and comparing the two differential equations for V_m and V_0 it is seen that the phase velocity has to be defined by the equation

$$\frac{W^2}{v^2} = 2m(W - U). \qquad [132]$$

Inserting the values for ω and v in the fundamental optical equation, Schrödinger's fundamental equation in wave mechanics is found to be

$$\nabla^2 \psi + \frac{8\pi^2 m}{h^2}(W - U)\psi = 0. \qquad [133]$$

The vibrational state is to be characterized by the function

$$\Psi = \psi e^{-i\omega t} = \psi e^{-i2\pi(W/h)t}. \qquad [133']$$

If now a mechanical picture of the system is known and therefore U is given as a function of the coordinates, it will be possible to construct

[4] E. Schrödinger, in a number of articles, which appeared in *Ann. Physik*, beginning (4) 79, 361 (1926). They are reprinted under the title: "Abhandlungen zur Wellenmechanik," J. A. Barth, Leipzig, 1927.

a corresponding picture of a vibrating system. The vibrations of this second system are supposed to be characterized by the wave function Ψ defined in [133] and [133′]. It is of course a hypothesis that we will be able to describe the natural behavior of a system by calculating properties of the corresponding vibratory system. The way in which Schrödinger's equation has been introduced suggests that possibly the factor $W - U$ multiplying ψ might only be the first term of a series arranged according to ascending powers of h, for this would not interfere with the correspondence to classical mechanics in the limit for $h = 0$. So far however this generalization has not presented itself as necessary.

Equation [133] enables us to calculate wave functions provided we consider the total energy W as a known quantity. For every value of W it will be possible to calculate corresponding functions ψ, and so far nothing has been said which would distinguish Bohr's characteristic stationary states from the others.

Now in a simple mechanical case like the vibrations of a string, the differential equation alone (for the displacement of a particle anywhere on the string) does not define the frequency of the proper vibrations of the string. We have to introduce the boundary conditions also. As an analogy to this Schrödinger introduces boundary conditions to define the proper vibrations of the vibrating system defined by [133]. He defines as proper vibrations those for which ψ is finite and single-valued over the whole range of the variables; which has to be considered from the physical point of view. This condition can only be fulfilled for definite values of the parameter W. Schrödinger considers these special values W_i of W as the energy of the stationary states, and the corresponding function ψ_i as the wave functions characteristic for these levels. In this way a set of vibrating systems is defined, which are supposed to contain the characteristics necessary to explain the natural behavior of the system under consideration. Heisenberg's treatment of quantum theory culminated also in the definition of such a set. Fortunately it can be shown that Born's general mathematical treatment of this case leads to the same set as Schrödinger's theory.

As every level is represented by the corresponding wave function we will expect that not only its energy but also other characteristic quantities, as, for instance, the probability of transition between different levels, will have to be calculated using the special form which ψ assumes as a solution of the fundamental equation. But for our immediate purpose, $i.e.$, the calculation of the dielectric constant, it has been seen in the foregoing chapter that a knowledge of the energy of the stationary states alone is sufficient. That is why we defer the description of phenomena more intimately connected with the mathematical expression for the wave function to a later Chapter IX.

CHAPTER IX

ROTATING MOLECULES

28. The Energy Levels of a Rotating Diatomic Molecule.

As an example for the application of the quantum rules discussed in the foregoing Section 27, we will treat the special case of diatomic gases in detail. With respect to the more general case of polyatomic gases we will only give some results and refer to the literature. A diatomic molecule like HCl may be considered as a rigid connection of two masses, with the moment of inertia A and the electric

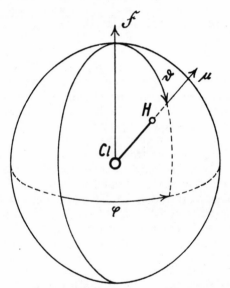

FIG. 31. Space coordinates of HCl dipole.

moment μ in the direction of the line connecting the masses.
The part ψ of the wave function

$$\Psi = \psi e^{-i(2\pi/h)Wt}$$

has to be a solution of the fundamental equation

$$\frac{1}{\sin \vartheta} \frac{\partial}{\partial \vartheta} \left(\sin \vartheta \frac{\partial \psi}{\partial \vartheta} \right) + \frac{1}{\sin^2 \vartheta} \frac{\partial^2 \psi}{\partial \varphi^2}$$
$$+ \frac{8\pi^2 A}{h^2} (W + \mu E \cos \vartheta)\psi = 0 \qquad [134]$$

if the angles ϑ, φ, characterizing the direction of the electric moment, are introduced in the usual way with respect to an axis determined by the electric intensity E; for the potential energy in this case is

$$U = -\mu E \cos \vartheta.$$

That this equation has the form appropriate for the special system characterized by the angles ϑ and φ may be inferred first from the fact that the differential operation contained in the two first terms of the left-hand side is the form of div grad, in polar angles on the sphere of radius unity. Secondly, a substitution

$$\psi = e^{(2\pi i/h)[V_0 + (h/2\pi i)V_1 + \cdots]}$$

will lead for V_0 to the Hamiltonian equation of classical mechanics in the limit $h = 0$. Also a single particle of mass m connected at an invariable distance a with a center O, about which it can rotate, may be treated. It will be seen that [133] goes over into [134] with

$$A = ma^2.$$

The general form of the equation for any kind of coordinates has been discussed by Schrödinger (loc. cit.), and it is identical with [134] in our special case.

We have to find such values of W for which ψ is finite on the whole sphere. These values will be equal to the energy of the stationary states. Let us introduce the energy quantum

$$u = \frac{h^2}{8\pi^2 A} \qquad [135]$$

and the two numerical parameters

$$\lambda = \frac{W}{u}; \quad \kappa = \frac{\mu E}{u}. \qquad [135']$$

Equation [134] can then be written in the form

$$\frac{1}{\sin \vartheta} \frac{\partial}{\partial \vartheta}\left(\sin \vartheta \frac{\partial \psi}{\partial \vartheta}\right) + \frac{1}{\sin^2 \vartheta} \frac{\partial^2 \psi}{\partial \varphi^2} + (\lambda + \kappa \cos \vartheta)\psi = 0. \qquad [136]$$

It will only be necessary to determine the characteristic values of λ for which ψ is finite, assuming κ to be small, as we are not interested now in saturation effects. Therefore we consider first the limiting case $\kappa = 0$. It is well known that the equation

$$\frac{1}{\sin \vartheta} \frac{\partial}{\partial \vartheta}\left(\sin \vartheta \frac{\partial \psi}{\partial \vartheta}\right) + \frac{1}{\sin^2 \vartheta} \frac{\partial^2 \psi}{\partial \varphi^2} + n(n+1)\psi = 0$$

defines spherical harmonics if n is any whole number including 0, and it has been shown that this is the only case in which ψ is finite over the whole sphere.[1] The energy of the different energy levels

[1] Compare, for instance, Courant-Hilbert, "Methoden der Mathematischen Physik," p. 421.

in the case $E = 0$ can therefore be calculated by

$$\lambda = n(n + 1) \qquad\qquad [137]$$

or

$$W = n(n + 1)\,\frac{h^2}{8\pi^2 A}\,. \qquad\qquad [137']$$

If we introduce the different spherical harmonics by substituting

$$\psi = \Theta \begin{cases} \cos p\varphi, \\ \sin p\varphi, \end{cases}$$

where Θ depends only on ϑ, and p is a whole number, the equation for Θ is

$$\frac{1}{\sin \vartheta}\,\frac{d}{d\vartheta}\left(\sin \vartheta\,\frac{d\Theta}{d\vartheta\circ} \right) + \left[n(n + 1) - \frac{p^2}{\sin^2 \vartheta} \right]\Theta = 0,$$

or, taking $\cos \vartheta = x$ as a new variable,

$$\frac{d}{dx}\left[(1 - x^2)\,\frac{d\Theta}{dx} \right] + \left[n(n + 1) - \frac{p^2}{1 - x^2} \right]\Theta = 0. \quad [138]$$

For $p = 0$ this is the equation of the ordinary zonal harmonics $P_n(x)$ which are polynomials in x, the highest power of x being n. It is easily shown that the solution of [138] for any value of p can be derived by the differentiation process,

$$P_n{}^p(x) = (1 - x^2)^{p/2}\,\frac{d^p}{dx^p}\,P_n(x). \qquad\qquad [139]$$

The index p cannot be larger than n, for this would reduce the right-hand member to zero.

If now we write the general spherical harmonic in the form

$$P_n{}^p(x) \begin{cases} \cos p\varphi, \\ \sin p\varphi, \end{cases}$$

we see that to every value of n correspond $2n + 1$ different harmonics. The ψ-function of the nth energy level, of energy value

$$n(n + 1)\,\frac{h^2}{8\pi^2 A}\,,$$

can be taken as the sum of these $2n + 1$ functions, each multiplied by an arbitrary constant. The ψ-function contains the $2n + 1$ arbitrary constants and this is the reason why the level has to be considered as a level of the multiplicity $2n + 1$. We have to expect that if we disturb the system, for instance in applying the field E each of these levels will split up.

We have now to consider the energy levels in a field E such that κ has a finite value. As is seen from [136], it is still possible to assume

$$\psi = \Theta \begin{cases} \cos p\varphi, \\ \sin p\varphi, \end{cases}$$

but now Θ has to be a solution of the equation

$$\frac{d}{dx}\left[(1 - x^2)\frac{d\Theta}{dx}\right] - \frac{p^2}{1 - x^2}\Theta + [\lambda + \kappa x]\Theta = 0. \quad [140]$$

Let us try a series made up of spherical harmonics of different order letting [2]

$$\Theta = \sum_n c_n P_n{}^p(x). \quad [141]$$

If we introduce this series in [140], we obtain the condition

$$\sum_n [\lambda - n(n + 1)]c_n P_n{}^p + \kappa \sum_n c_n x P_n{}^p = 0, \quad [142]$$

taking into account the differential equation [138], of which $P_n{}^p$ is a solution. But in the theory of spherical harmonics it is shown that

$$(2n + 1)x P_n{}^p = (n + p)P_{n-1}^p + (n + 1 - p)P_{n+1}^p. \quad [143]$$

Introducing this relation in [142], we can arrange the left-hand side as a series of harmonics $P_n{}^p$, and if this series is zero every coefficient must be zero. This gives the condition

$$\kappa \frac{n - p}{2n - 1}c_{n-1} + [\lambda - n(n + 1)]c_n + \kappa \frac{n + 1 + p}{2n + 3}c_{n+1} = 0. \quad [144]$$

If $\kappa = 0$, we fall back of course on the former condition

$$\lambda = n(n + 1)$$

and it remains to be seen what the condition on λ must be for the equations [144] to hold when $\kappa \neq 0$. We may suspect that each of the roots λ, which we are going to consider, may develop continuously from any of the roots $n(n + 1)$ found in the case $\kappa = 0$. Let us fix our attention on one of these roots

$$\lambda_0 = n_0(n_0 + 1).$$

We will then try the series

$$\lambda = \lambda_0 + \kappa\lambda_1 + \kappa^2\lambda_2 + \cdots. \quad [145]$$

[2] The coefficients c_n are of course dependent on p, but as p is constant in the sum, we do not express the dependence by writing $c_n{}^p$ instead of c_n.

Since at the same time the coefficients c_n will be functions of κ, we try the series

$$\left.\begin{array}{rl}
c_{n_0} =& c_{n_0}^{(0)} + c_{n_0}^{(1)}\kappa + c_{n_0}^{(2)}\kappa^2 + \cdots \\[4pt]
c_{n_0-1} =& \qquad c_{n_0-1}^{(1)}\kappa + c_{n_0-1}^{(2)}\kappa^2 + \cdots \\[4pt]
c_{n_0+1} =& \qquad c_{n_0+1}^{(1)}\kappa + c_{n_0+1}^{(2)}\kappa^2 + \cdots \\[4pt]
c_{n_0-2} =& \qquad\qquad c_{n_0-2}^{(2)}\kappa^2 + \cdots \\[4pt]
c_{n_0+2} =& \qquad\qquad c_{n_0+2}^{(2)}\kappa^2 + \cdots
\end{array}\right\} \qquad [146]$$

In the case $\kappa = 0$ the coefficient c_{n_0} was the only one existent; therefore we begin the series with a constant. For the two coefficients next to this, i.e., c_{n_0-1} and c_{n_0+1}, we assume a series beginning with κ. The two coefficients next to these, i.e., c_{n_0-2} and c_{n_0+2}, we assume of the order κ^2, etc. It is readily seen from [144] that this is possible. We will perform the calculation for the first root $\lambda_0 = 0$. This will give us the energy of the level $n = 0$; that is, the energy obtained in a field by those molecules which have no energy at all in the undisturbed state. The only value of p which has to be considered is $p = 0$. The equations [144] have now the form

$$\left.\begin{array}{l}
\lambda c_0 + \dfrac{\kappa}{3} c_1 = 0, \\[10pt]
\kappa c_0 + (\lambda - 2)c_1 + \dfrac{2}{5}\kappa c_2 = 0, \\[10pt]
\dfrac{2}{3}\kappa c_1 + (\lambda - 6)c_2 + \dfrac{3}{7}\kappa c_3 = 0.
\end{array}\right\} \qquad [144']$$

From the first of these equations it is seen at once that the series for λ has in this case to begin with a term proportional to κ^2. We therefore assume as a special case of [146]:

$$\begin{aligned}
\lambda &= \lambda_2 \kappa^2, \\
c_0 &= c_0^{(0)} + \cdots, \\
c_1 &= c_1^{(1)}\kappa + \cdots, \\
c_2 &= c_2^{(2)}\kappa^2 + \cdots.
\end{aligned}$$

Substituting these equations in [144'] and confining our attention to the terms of lowest order in κ in the first two equations, we obtain

$$\left.\begin{array}{l}
\kappa^2 \{\lambda_2 c_0^{(0)} + \frac{1}{3}c_1^{(1)}\} = 0, \\[6pt]
\kappa\{c_0^{(0)} - 2c_1^{(1)}\} = 0.
\end{array}\right\} \qquad [147]$$

This is only possible if

$$\lambda_2 = -\tfrac{1}{6}$$

and therefore

$$\lambda = -\frac{\kappa^2}{6}, \qquad [148]$$

showing that a molecule which has no energy at all outside of the field will obtain the energy

$$W = \lambda u = -\frac{1}{6}\frac{8\pi^2}{h^2}A\mu^2E^2$$

in the field of intensity E.[3] The above method may be applied to each energy level in turn and the general expression for λ is found to be

$$\lambda = n(n+1) + \left[\Phi_n^p - \Phi_{n+1}^p\right]\frac{\kappa}{2}, \qquad [149]$$

where

$$\Phi_n^p = \frac{(n-p)(n+p)}{n(2n-1)(2n+1)}. \qquad [149']$$

In the general case it is seen that the second term in the series for λ is again of the order κ^2. Substitute

$$\lambda = n_0(n_0+1) + \lambda_2\kappa^2,$$
$$c_{n_0} = c_{n_0}^{(0)} + \dots,$$
$$c_{n_0-1} = c_{n_0-1}^{(1)}\kappa + \dots,$$
$$c_{n_0+1} = c_{n_0+1}^{(1)}\kappa + \dots,$$

and retain the terms of lowest order in the three equations for $n = n_0$, $n = n_0 + 1$ and $n = n_0 - 1$. The result is

$$\lambda_2 c_{n_0}^{(0)} + \frac{n_0 - p}{2n_0 - 1}c_{n_0-1}^{(1)} + \frac{n_0 + 1 + p}{2n_0 + 3}c_{n_0+1}^{(1)} = 0,$$

$$\left[n_0(n_0+1) - (n_0-1)n_0\right]c_{n_0-1}^{(1)} + \frac{n_0 + p}{2n_0 + 1}c_{n_0}^{(0)} = 0,$$

$$\left[n_0(n_0+1) - (n_0+1)(n_0+2)\right]c_{n_0+1}^{(1)} + \frac{n_0 + 1 - p}{2n_0 + 1}c_{n_0}^{(0)} = 0.$$

If $c_{n_0+1}^{(1)}$ and $c_{n_0-1}^{(1)}$ are calculated from the last two equations and substituted in the first, it is seen that

$$\lambda_2 = \Phi_{n_0}^p - \Phi_{n_0+1}^p.$$

As n_0 can have all values, we omitted the index in the text.

We can summarize the result in the following way. The level $n = 0$ of multiplicity 1 is shifted to the energy value $W_{0,\,0}$ given by the equation

$$\frac{W_{0,\,0}}{u} = -\frac{\kappa^2}{6}.$$

[3] See the definition of λ, u and κ in [135] and [135'].

The level $n = 1$ of multiplicity 3 is split in two levels

$$\frac{W_{1,\,0}}{u} = 2 + \frac{2^{-}}{20}\,\kappa^2,$$

$$\frac{W_{1,\,1}}{u} = 2 - \frac{1}{20}\,\kappa^2.$$

The first of these new levels, corresponding to $n = 1$, $p = 0$, has the multiplicity 1, since $\sin p\varphi$ vanishes for $p = 0$ and of the two functions $P_n{}^p$ $\begin{cases} \cos p\varphi \\ \sin p\varphi \end{cases}$ only one is left. The second level corresponding to $n = 1$, $p = 1$, has the multiplicity 2. The first has a larger energy in the field than outside, the corresponding molecule behaving therefore as if it had a negative polarizability; that is, it is analogous to a *diamagnetic* particle in a magnetic field. The molecule corresponding to the second level behaves normally.

The level $n = 2$ of multiplicity 5 is split in 3 levels

$$\frac{W_{2,\,0}}{u} = 6 + \frac{2}{84}\,\kappa^2,$$

$$\frac{W_{2,\,1}}{u} = 6 + \frac{1}{84}\,\kappa^2,$$

$$\frac{W_{2,\,2}}{u} = 6 - \frac{2}{84}\,\kappa^2.$$

The first is of multiplicity 1, the two others of multiplicity 2. The arrangement of the levels is represented by Figure 32 in the usual manner. In the left part are seen the undisturbed and in the right part the disturbed levels. If we take the shift of every sublevel for one value of n, multiply every shift with the corresponding multiplicity and add these values together, we find zero. This is true in general. We will express this in saying that the center of gravity of the levels n is not influenced by the field. In the next section we will see that this is the reason why only the molecules of energy zero contribute to the dielectric constant of the gas.

29. The Dielectric Constant of Polar Gases.

To find the average electric moment of a molecule of the kind for which the energy levels have been calculated in Section 28, we have only to apply the general equation [112]. The sums σ_0, σ_1 and σ_2 appearing in this equation are defined by [109]. The energy which we called $w_i{}^*$ in these equations is the energy of the level i if undisturbed, as is seen from [108], while the quantities μ_i and α_i are the coefficients entering in the development of the energy in powers of E. In our case it was found that the change in λ is proportional to κ^2, that is, proportional to E^2. Diatomic gases can therefore show no linear Stark effect in the spectral lines corresponding to a transition between the different rotational states. Although

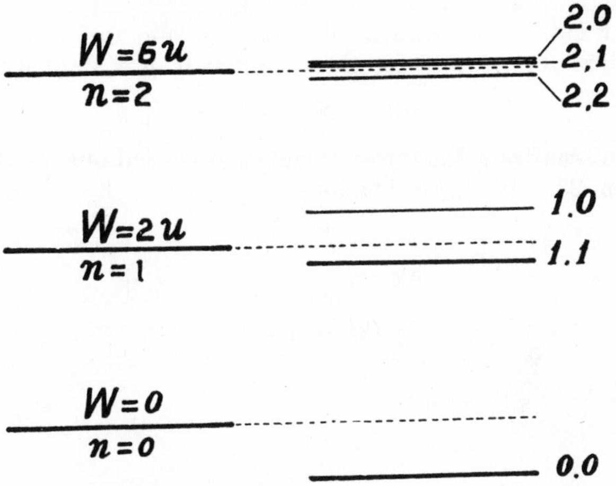

$$W=6u \qquad n=2$$

$$\begin{matrix} 2.0 \\ 2.1 \\ 2.2 \end{matrix}$$

$$W=2u \qquad n=1$$

$$\begin{matrix} 1.0 \\ 1.1 \end{matrix}$$

$$W=0 \qquad n=0$$

$$0.0$$

Fig. 32.   Effect of an electric field on the energy levels.

instead of one index i we have now two indices n and p, the energy values w_i^* are identical with

$$n(n+1)u$$

and are thus independent of the second index.   The different sums appearing in [109] are seen to be represented in the following way:

$$\left.\begin{aligned} \sigma_0 &= \sum_{n=0}^{\infty} (2n+1)e^{-n(n+1)(u/kT)}, \\ \sigma_1 &= \sigma_2'' = 0, \\ \sigma_2 &= -\frac{\mu^2}{u} \sum_{n=0}^{\infty} e^{-n(n+1)(u/kT)} \sum_{p=-n}^{+n} (\Phi_n{}^p - \Phi_{n+1}^p). \end{aligned}\right\} \quad [150]$$

In the first of these sums we have already performed the summation with respect to p in introducing the multiplicity factor $(2n+1)$. In the last sum we take account of all possible levels in giving to p all values from $-n$ to $+n$.   As only p^2 enters in the definition [149'] of $\Phi_n{}^p$, this amounts to assigning the multiplicity 1 to the level with $p = 0$, and the multiplicity 2 to a level with any other value of p.

It is well known that

$$\sum_{p=-n}^{+n} p^2 = n^2 + (n-1)^2 + \cdots + 0 + 1^2 + 2^2 + \cdots + n^2$$
$$= \tfrac{1}{3}n(n+1)(2n+1).$$

Hence

$$\sum_{p=-n}^{+n} \Phi_n{}^p = (2n + 1)\frac{n^2}{n(2n - 1)(2n + 1)} - \frac{1}{3}\frac{n(n + 1)(2n + 1)}{n(2n - 1)(2n + 1)} = \frac{1}{3}.$$

Since this sum is independent of n, the last sum appearing in [150] is therefore zero, except for the case $n = 0$, $p = 0$, in which case

$$\Phi_n{}^p - \Phi_{n+1}^p = -\tfrac{1}{3},$$

as is also seen from the direct calculation carried out for this level in Section 28. We have therefore

$$\left. \begin{aligned} \sigma_2 &= \frac{\mu^2}{3u}, \\ \sigma_0 &= \sum_{n=0}^{\infty} (2n + 1)e^{-n(n+1)(u/kT)}. \end{aligned} \right\} \qquad [151]$$

Applying [112], it is found that

$$m = \frac{\dfrac{\mu^2}{3u} E}{\sum_{n=0}^{\infty} (2n + 1)e^{-n(n+1)(u/kT)}},$$

or if we introduce

$$\xi = \frac{u}{kT} \qquad [152]$$

we have

$$m = \frac{\mu^2}{3kT} E \frac{1}{\xi \sum_{n=0}^{\infty} (2n + 1)e^{-n(n+1)\xi}}. \qquad [153]$$

The molar polarization will be $(4\pi/3)N$ times the coefficient of E in [153]. The quantity ξ is a numeric. Let us introduce a temperature T_k, characteristic for the molecule, by the definition

$$kT_k = u = \frac{h^2}{8\pi^2 A}. \qquad [154]$$

ξ is then

$$\xi = \frac{T_k}{T}, \qquad [154']$$

and the average moment will be materially different if the temperature is small or if it is large compared with the characteristic temperature. The HCl molecule has a relatively small moment of inertia A, the distance between the two masses being 1.27×10^{-8}

cm. (compare Section 13); the corresponding moment of inertia A introduced in [154] gives for the characteristic temperature $T_k = 14.7$. At ordinary temperatures ξ is therefore small for HCl and will be still smaller for other molecules with larger moments of inertia. In this case the denominator in [153] can be calculated by integration,

$$\xi \sum_{n=0}^{\infty} (2n + 1)e^{-n(n+1)\xi} = \xi \int_{0}^{\infty} (2n + 1)e^{-n(n+1)\xi} dn = \xi \left[\frac{e^{-n(n+1)\xi}}{-\xi} \right]_{0}^{\infty} = 1,$$

and we find the same result as in the classical theory,[4] namely,

$$m = \frac{\mu^2}{3kT} E. \qquad [155]$$

To a second approximation it may be shown that

$$m = \frac{\mu^2}{3kT} \left(1 - \frac{1}{3} \frac{T_k}{T} \right) E. \qquad [155']$$

It seems very difficult to detect the deviations due to quantization as they are expressed in the difference between the equations [155] and [155']. For this purpose experiments at relatively low temperature have to be made, even for HCl the difference being less than 2 per cent at 0° Centigrade, and in this case association effects will be much more effective than the quantum effect, unless special care is taken to eliminate association by keeping the density of the gas very low. The dependence of the polarizability on the temperature expressed in [155] can be explained by saying that, whereas only molecules of rotational energy zero with a constant polarizability contribute to the polarization, it is the number of these molecules which decreases with increasing temperature.

At a first glance this statement seems to be very different from the explanation offered for the temperature variation in classical theory. That such a difference however does not exist is seen if the classical calculation is arranged in a way more similar to the method followed in quantum theory.[5] Let us call the momenta p_1 and p_2 corresponding to the angles ϑ and φ, and write for the potential energy

$$U = - \mu E(1 + \cos \vartheta).$$

[4] A first introduction of quantum theory in this field was tried by W. Pauli, Z. Physik, 6, 319 (1921) and by L. Pauling, Proc. Nat. Acad. Wash., 12, 32 (1926); Phys. Rev., 27, 568 (1926). The result was that the factor in [155] came out to be different from 1/3. As soon as quantum theory had taken the new form given to it by Heisenberg and Born, it was calculated by L. Mensing and W. Pauli, Physik. Z., 27, 509 (1926), and by R. de Kronig, Proc. Nat. Acad. Wash., 12, 488 (1926), who found that in this theory the factor was again 1/3. The same result was found applying wave mechanics by C. Manneback, Physik. Z., 27, 563 (1926).

[5] W. Alexandrow, Physik. Z., 22, 258 (1921).

We have then counted U in such a way that $U = 0$ if $\vartheta = \pi$, that is, if the electric moment and the field are oppositely directed. The total energy is

$$W = \frac{1}{2A}\left(p_1{}^2 + \frac{p_2{}^2}{\sin^2 \vartheta} \right) - \mu E(1 + \cos \vartheta)$$

and the average electric moment will be given in classical theory by the expression

$$\overline{m} = C \int \int \int \int e^{-(W/kT)} \mu \cos \vartheta d\vartheta d\varphi dp_1 dp_2.$$

The integration with respect to φ can be performed at once since W is independent of φ. Instead of p_1 and p_2 we introduce two new variables B and β by the equations

$$\begin{cases} p_1 = \sqrt{2A}\ B^{1/2} \cos \beta, \\ p_2 = \sqrt{2A}\ B^{1/2} \sin \vartheta \sin \beta. \end{cases}$$

The variable B has then the meaning of the total kinetic energy and β is an angle. To cover all possible positive and negative values of p_1 and p_2 we have to vary B between 0 and ∞ and the angle β from 0 to 2π. Instead of the product $dp_1 dp_2$ we have to introduce $A \sin \vartheta dB d\beta$. We have then

$$\overline{m} = 4\pi^2 \mu AC \int \int e^{-(1/kT)\{B - \mu E(1 + \cos \vartheta)\}} \cos \vartheta \sin \vartheta d\vartheta dB.$$

Suppose now we fix our attention on molecules with a definite orientation ϑ. They can still have all values for their kinetic energy B. Then let us perform the integration with respect to B in two steps, the first going from $B = 0$ to $B = B^*$ and the second from $B = B^*$ to $B = \infty$. The formula for the moment now assumes the form

$$\overline{m} = 4\pi^2 \mu AC \int_0^\pi \cos \vartheta \sin \vartheta d\vartheta e^{+(\mu E/kT)(1 + \cos \vartheta)} \left[\int_0^{B^*} e^{-(B/kT)} dB \right. $$
$$\left. + \int_{B^*}^\infty e^{-(B/kT)} dB \right].$$

If then we take

$$B^* = \mu E(1 + \cos \vartheta),$$

the second integral in the brackets will be equal to

$$kTe^{-(B^*/kT)} = kTe^{-(\mu E/kT)(1 + \cos \vartheta)}$$

and by the succeeding integration with respect to ϑ this term will vanish altogether. Therefore

$$\overline{m} = 4\pi^2\mu AC \int_0^\pi \cos\vartheta \sin\vartheta d\vartheta e^{(\mu E/kT)(1+\cos\vartheta)} \int_0^{B^*} e^{-(B/kT)} dB,$$

and this can be interpreted by saying that of all the molecules with orientation ϑ only those will contribute to the polarization whose kinetic energy B is not larger than B^*. Now as is readily seen B^* is the energy necessary to turn the molecule from the angle ϑ to π. All the molecules which have enough kinetic energy to overcome the critical orientation $\vartheta = \pi$ are ineffective. Only those which left to themselves would oscillate between two extreme positions contribute to the average moment. It is clear that the classical result stated in this way is a perfect analogue to the result of quantum theory. The higher quantum levels are ineffective not because they are not influenced by the field, but because this influence is partly positive, partly negative, and an exact compensation occurs for every level. If we are interested in this effect, a measurement of the dielectric constant will be of no use. But if the experiment of Stern and Gerlach is done with polar molecules in a non-homogeneous electric field, we have to expect that the molecular ray is partly attracted to and partly repelled from regions where the square of the field intensity is large.[6] There will however be one deviation from the calculated formulas. They are based on the assumption of rigid molecules, that is, no distortion effect has been taken into account. It is very probable that the distortion will only introduce an additive constant to the polarizability, as it did in classical theory. The molecular ray will therefore show an attraction, due to distortion, to places where the square of the field intensity is large, superposed on the effect due to the permanent moment. For the special case that the distortion is assumed to be merely due to a displacement of the two atoms with different charges (for instance, H and Cl in HCl) the calculation has been carried out and has confirmed our supposition.[7]

The calculations of the wave function and the stationary energy levels become more complicated for molecules consisting of more than two atoms. For the case of molecules having two equal moments of inertia, such that instead of three moments $A\ B\ C$ we have the three moments $A\ A\ C$, the calculation has been performed using Born's method [8] and also Schrödinger's method.[9] The

[6] Experiments of this kind have been made by E. Wrede, Z. Physik, **44**, 261 (1927), in Stern's laboratory. They have given the expected result.

[7] R. Gans, Physik. Z., **28**, 309 (1927); C. Manneback, ibid., **28**, 514 (1927).

[8] R. de L. Kronig, Proc. Nat. Acad. Wash., **12**, 608 (1926).

[9] C. Manneback, Physik. Z., **28**, 72 (1927); F. Reiche, Z. Physik, **39**, 444 (1926), calculated only the terms of first order corresponding to the linear Stark effect.

molecule NH_3 would be an example for this case. If we introduce again the energy quantum

$$u = \frac{h^2}{8\pi^2 A}$$

and the numeric

$$\kappa = \frac{\mu E}{u},$$

it is found that the energy values W of the stationary states are given by the equation

$$\frac{W}{u} = \left[n(n+1) + \frac{A-C}{C} q^2 \right] - \kappa \frac{pq}{n(n+1)} \\ + \frac{\kappa^2}{2} \left[\Psi_{n,\,p,\,q} - \Psi_{n+1,\,p,\,q} \right]. \qquad [156]$$

The quantum numbers n, p, q are whole numbers; n can have all values from 0 to ∞, while for a given value of n the numbers p and q range from $-n$ to $+n$, and the function $\Psi_{n,\,p,\,q}$ is defined by the equation

$$\Psi_{n,\,p,\,q} = \frac{(n^2 - p^2)(n^2 - q^2)}{n^3(2n-1)(2n+1)}. \qquad [156']$$

In the special case $n = 0$, $p = 0$, $q = 0$, however, we have instead of [156] the equation

$$\frac{W_{0,\,0,\,0}}{u} = -\frac{1}{3}\frac{\kappa^2}{2}. \qquad [156'']$$

It is seen that neither the linear nor the quadratic Stark effect depends on the value of the moment of inertia C. The linear effect is also independent of A, and its measurement would therefore give an opportunity to determine the electric moment μ at once.[10]

It is easy to get an estimate of the magnitude of the splitting of the rotational band lines of a polyatomic symmetrical polar molecule in an electric field F, which in turn gives a direct measurement of the electric moment μ. The value of the splitting of the terms is proportional to μF, the proportionality factor being a pure numerical, depending only on the three rotational quantum numbers of the molecule and being the *same* for all symmetrical polyatomic molecules (Manneback, *loc. cit.*, p. 153). Taking $\mu = 10^{-18}$ e.s.u. and $F = 50,000$ volts/cm. yields $\mu F = 1.66 \times 10^{-16}$ ergs.

We compare this to the energy difference of the terms which corresponds to the distance between two consecutive lines in *any* rotational band spectrum of a molecule, say, whose three moments of inertia are each equal to $A = 3 \times 10^{-40}$. This energy difference

[10] P. Debye and C. Manneback, *Nature*, **119**, 83 (1927).

amounts to $h^2/4\pi^2A = 3.6 \times 10^{-15}$ ergs. The order of magnitude of the splitting in the considered case therefore is nearly a *twentieth* of the distance between two consecutive lines in the band spectrum, which seems quite accessible to the measurements.

The preceding does not apply to diatomic molecules, as the Stark effect is then no more proportional to the first power of the electric intensity. How this can be reconciled with the fact that the calculated splitting is independent of the form (ratio of polar to equatorial moments of inertia) of the symmetrical molecule is discussed by Manneback (*loc. cit.*, p. 153).

If now the average electric moment is again calculated following the same method as before, it is found that with the same degree of approximation

$$\overline{m} = \frac{\mu^2}{3kT} E.$$

In a second approximation the departure is the same as for diatomic gases and is independent of the value of C.[11] Thus the classical factor $\frac{1}{3}$ holds also in this more general case.

Finally J. H. Van Vleck following another method has shown that the factor $\frac{1}{3}$ must be expected to hold in the most general case.[12] The results of the quantum theory in its most modern form prove to be much more closely connected with the classical theory. From a practical point of view it is important to note that the absolute values of the permanent moments, which have been calculated applying the classical theory, will need no change.

[11] *Compare* C. Manneback, *loc. cit.*, p. 79.
[12] J. H. Van Vleck, *Phys. Rev.*, **29**, 727 (1927).

CHAPTER X

DISPERSION AND ABSORPTION OF POLAR GASES

30. Probabilities of Transition.

Up to this section our demands upon wave mechanics have been limited in that we have only asked for the evaluation of the energy levels. Indeed this furnished sufficient information for the calculation of the dielectric constant and would be equally sufficient if we asked, for instance, for the dependence of the specific heat upon the temperature. We now propose to give a short discussion of the main features of the radiation and absorption we have to expect, confining our attention to the special case of rotating molecules of the kind of the HCl molecules.

We have seen that in this case every stationary state n, p could be characterized by a wave function

$$\Psi_{n,\,p} = \psi_{n,\,p}(\vartheta,\ \varphi)e^{-i(2\pi/hW)_{n,p}t}. \qquad [157]$$

In the special case $E = 0$, the energy of the level n, p is

$$W_{n,\,p} = n(n + 1)u = n(n + 1)\frac{h^2}{8\pi^2 A} \qquad [158]$$

and

$$\psi_{n,\,p} = c_{n,\,p}P_n{}^p \begin{cases} \sin p\varphi, \\ \cos p\varphi, \end{cases} \qquad [159]$$

where $c_{n,\,p}$ is an arbitrary constant. According to Bohr's principle radiation occurs by a transition from one state to another and the frequency is given by the general equation

$$h\nu = W' - W.$$

Suppose now that we multiply the wave function $\psi_{n,\,p}$ corresponding to the level n, p, with the conjugate value of a wave function $\psi_{n',\,p'}$ corresponding to another level n', p'. We will then obtain a new function

$$\Psi_{n,\,p}\overline{\Psi}_{n',\,p'} = \psi_{n,\,p}\psi_{n',\,p'}e^{i(2\pi/h)(W_{n',\,p'}-W_{n,\,p})t},$$

which, according to Bohr's principle, represents a vibration of the frequency demanded by this principle. The question arises at once if the product $\psi_{n,\,p}\psi_{n',\,p'}$, which in our case is a function of the coordinates ϑ, φ on the sphere, may be in some way characteristic for the radiation, which we know to have the frequency

$$\nu = \frac{W_{n',\,p'} - W_{n,\,p}}{h}.$$

Schrödinger's hypothesis is that the product $\psi\psi'$ may be taken to represent something proportional to a density of electricity; it is made in analogy to a similar calculation in the theory of Heisenberg and Born. In our case $\psi\psi'$ would represent a density of electricity distributed over the surface of a sphere. The meaning is that if we calculate the radiation due to the distribution

$$\psi\psi' e^{i(2\pi/h)(W'-W)t},$$

which vibrates with the frequency corresponding to the transition W' to W, applying the classical principles contained in the equations of Maxwell, we will have found the characteristics and especially the intensity of the natural radiation. From a physical point of view it is to prefer to interpret the product as giving the probability for the system to be in the state defined by the coordinates of which ψ is a function. As however the interpretation does not call for a change in the calculations, we will not enter into this question.

So far however we are hindered by the fact that the function ψ contains an arbitrary constant. To eliminate this constant it will be assumed that ψ is normalized, i.e., the constant will be taken such that ψ^2 integrated over the whole range of the variables equals unity. In our case then

$$\int \psi^2 d\Omega = 1, \qquad [160]$$

where $d\Omega$ is a surface element of the sphere of radius unity. We cannot expect however that this is all, for in our case the intensity of radiation will certainly depend on the magnitude of the electric moment μ, and the amplitude of the vibrations is expected to be proportional to μ. Having normalized the functions ψ, we will finally take for the density of electricity on the sphere with radius unity the function

$$\mu\psi\psi' e^{i(2\pi/h)(W'-W)t}.$$

It follows from the equations of Maxwell that the radiation of a vibrating system at a great distance can be expressed by the three electric moments of the system in three rectangular directions. We will define, for instance, the electric moment vibrating in the direction of E by calculating

$$\int \mu\psi\psi' \cos \vartheta d\Omega e^{i(2\pi/h)(W'-W)t} \qquad [161]$$

and suppose that the classical radiation due to this moment is equivalent to the part of the natural radiation for which the electric intensity is directed in the planes containing the direction of E. The other parts of the radiation will be defined by the two remaining moments in a similar way. If we use the language of stationary states and transitions, we have to say that, as the calculated intensity will be proportional to the squares of the amplitudes of these moments, these squares will define the probability of transition. The procedure is equivalent to Schrödinger's procedure in the case of a moving electron. It might be that a numerical factor remained to be introduced in [161]. It can however be shown that, if we define ψ in the way we did with the numerical factor 1, the radiation calculated by [161] is just equal to the classical radiation for a rotating permanent moment μ in the limit for $h = 0$.[1] That is why it is believed that the factor has to be unity. Let us now calculate the normalizing coefficients $c_{n, p}$ and the amplitudes of the electric moments in our special case. We confine our attention to the limiting case of small values of E, in which the wave function can be supposed represented by a single harmonic. The coefficients $c_{n, p}$ are defined by [160], i.e.,

$$c_{n, p}^2 \int \int [P_n^p(x) \cos p\varphi]^2 dx d\varphi = 1,$$

if we substitute again x for $\cos \vartheta$. Performing the integration, it is found that

$$c_{n, p}^2 = \frac{1}{\pi} \frac{2n + 1}{2} \frac{(n - p)!}{(n + p)!} \qquad [162]$$

except for $p = 0$, in which case

$$c_{n, 0}^2 = \frac{1}{2\pi} \frac{2n + 1}{2}. \qquad [162']$$

If we introduce a system of rectangular coordinates in such a way that the z-axis is parallel to E and call the amplitudes of the three vibrating moments m_x, m_y and m_z, it is found that

$$m_z = \mu c_{n, p} c_{n', p'} \int \int x P_n^p P_{n'}^{p'} \begin{Bmatrix} \cos p\varphi \cos p'\varphi \\ \cos p\varphi \sin p'\varphi \\ \sin p\varphi \cos p'\varphi \\ \sin p\varphi \sin p'\varphi \end{Bmatrix} dx d\varphi. \qquad [163]$$

Supposing n, n' and p given, it is then seen at once that m_z will be zero except for the case in which $p' = p$. Our vibrating sphere will therefore give no radiation at all unless this condition is satisfied. This has been expressed in stating that transitions from p' to another p are "forbidden" transitions. Letting now $p' = p$, we apply the recurrence relation

$$(2n + 1)x P_n^p = (n - p + 1)P_{n+1}^p + (n + p)P_{n-1}^p,$$

and as spherical harmonics are orthogonal we see that n' also cannot be arbitrary, but has to be either $n + 1$ or $n - 1$ if m_z shall have a value different from zero. For our purpose it is sufficient to note

[1] Compare with the corresponding calculation for a charge with one degree of freedom, P. Debye, *Physik. Z.*, **28**, 170 (1927).

that m_z has only finite values if

$$p' = p \quad \text{and} \quad n' = \begin{cases} n - 1 \\ n + 1 \end{cases}$$

without calculating the magnitude of m.[2]

To calculate m_x, an expression has to be evaluated, which we obtain in replacing $x = \cos \vartheta$ by $\sin \vartheta \cos \vartheta$ in equation [163]. It can be shown, using the recurrence relation

$$(2n + 1) \sin \vartheta \, P_n{}^p = P_{n+1}{}^{p+1} - P_{n-1}{}^{p+1},$$

that $m_x = 0$ unless

$$p' = \begin{cases} p - 1 \\ p + 1 \end{cases} \quad \text{and} \quad n' = \begin{cases} n - 1 \\ n + 1. \end{cases}$$

Finally we see that only transitions between adjacent levels ($n' = n - 1$ or $n + 1$) are possible, and as the energy of the level n is

$$n(n + 1)u,$$

emission lines will be situated at the frequencies

$$\nu = [n(n + 1) - n(n - 1)]\frac{u}{h} = 2n\frac{h}{8\pi^2 A},$$

and the frequencies of the absorption lines will be expressed in a similar way. To close this very incomplete treatment of the probability of transition the following picture (Fig. 33) is given. Beginning with the level $n = 0$, the different levels are pictured as points with ordinates roughly proportional to their energy values. The full lines indicate possible transitions which correspond to a moment vibrating in the direction of E, while the dotted lines correspond to transitions characterized by a moment vibrating perpendicular to E.

31. The Wave Functions of Polar Molecules Disturbed by a Periodic Field.

At the end of Section 30 we found the frequencies of the lines which will appear as absorption lines in the infra-red part of the spectrum. Nearer to the visible part there will be a band spectrum due to the superposition of the vibrations of the dipole and its rotation. Having treated the molecule as rigid, this second spectrum therefore does not appear in our calculation.[3] The same applies for the following calculation. If now infra-red light is passed through

[2] To calculate the absolute value of the infra-red absorption in a polar gas, the values of m have to be known [compare R. Tolman and R. Badger, *Phys. Rev.*, 27, 383 (1927)].

[3] See for the more general case E. Fuess, *Ann. Physik*, (4) 80, 367 (1926); 81, 281 (1926).

the gas, we will expect that the refraction due to the rotation alone will become especially noticeable if we approach one of the absorption lines. The index of refraction is the square root of the dielectric

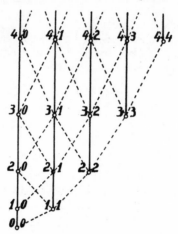

Fig. 33. Transitions between energy levels.

constant for the particular frequency under consideration and this quantity is known if we are able to calculate the electric moment vibrating with this frequency, which is equivalent to our molecule and its possible transitions. As we had to deal with the ordinary dielectric constant, we had to calculate the disturbance of the wave function by a constant field. If it is possible to calculate the disturbance by a periodic field, we should be able to calculate the polarization and therefore the refractivity index of the gas. If we confine our attention again to diatomic gases, we remember that for a constant field E the part of the wave function dependent on the coordinates was a solution of the equation

$$\nabla^2 \psi - 2A \left(\frac{2\pi i}{h} \right)^2 (W + \mu E \cos \vartheta) \psi = 0, \qquad [164]$$

where the operation ∇^2 has to be interpreted on the surface of the sphere of unit radius. This equation contains the total energy W and it is obvious that in this form we cannot apply it to a periodic field. Following Schrödinger (*loc. cit.*), we will therefore eliminate this quantity from [164]. The wave function is

$$\Psi = \psi(\vartheta, \varphi) e^{-i(2\pi/h)Wt}.$$

If we differentiate with respect to t, we have

$$\frac{\partial \Psi}{\partial t} = \frac{2\pi i}{h} W \Psi.$$

The equation [164] can then also be written in the form

$$\nabla^2\Psi + 2A\frac{2\pi i}{h}\frac{\partial\Psi}{\partial t} - 2A\left(\frac{2\pi i}{h}\right)^2\mu E\cos\vartheta\,\Psi = 0, \qquad [165]$$

in which W does not appear explicitly. Schrödinger makes the assumption that the form [165] can be applied to the general case that E is not constant but varies with the time. We assume

$$E = E_0\cos 2\pi\nu t \qquad [166]$$

and will have to find a solution Ψ of [165] in the limiting case of a small disturbing field, i.e., E_0 sufficiently small. We therefore assume

$$\Psi = \Psi_0 + G, \qquad [167]$$

where Ψ_0 is one of the wave functions

$$\Psi_0 = c_{n,\,p}P_n{}^p\left\{\begin{matrix}\cos p\varphi \\ \sin p\varphi\end{matrix}\right\}e^{-(2\pi i/h)W_{n,\,p}t},$$

which satisfies the conditions for undisturbed molecules, and G will be proportional to the small intensity E_0. We will indicate any harmonic with the indices n, p by $S_{n,\,p}$,

$$S_{n,\,p} = P_n{}^p\left\{\begin{matrix}\cos p\varphi \\ \sin p\varphi\end{matrix}\right.$$

We know then that this function is a solution of the equation

$$\nabla^2 S_{n,\,p} + n(n+1)S_{n,\,p} = 0. \qquad [168]$$

Observing this relation and confining our attention to first order terms in E_0, we will find for G the linear equation

$$\left.\begin{aligned}
\nabla^2 G + 2A&\frac{2\pi i}{h}\frac{\partial G}{\partial t} \\
&= A\left(\frac{2\pi i}{h}\right)^2\mu E_0\cos\vartheta c_{n,\,p}S_{n,\,p}\big[e^{-(2\pi i/h)(W_{n,\,p}+h\nu)t} \\
&\qquad\qquad + e^{-(2\pi i/h)(W_{n,\,p}-h\nu)t}\big],
\end{aligned}\right\} \qquad [169]$$

if we introduce [167] in the fundamental equation [165]. To solve this equation we can split G in two parts

$$G = g_1 e^{-(2\pi i/h)(W_{n,\,p}+h\nu)t} + g_2 e^{-(2\pi i/h)(W_{n,\,p}-h\nu)t}, \qquad [170]$$

and we will have for g_1 and g_2 the equations

$$
\left.
\begin{aligned}
\nabla^2 g_1 + \frac{8\pi^2 A}{h^2}(W_{n,\,p} + h\nu)g_1 &= -\frac{8\pi^2 A}{h^2}\frac{\mu E_0}{2}c_{n,\,p}\cos\vartheta S_{n,\,p}, \\
\nabla^2 g_2 + \frac{8\pi^2 A}{h^2}(W_{n,\,p} - h\nu)g_2 &= -\frac{8\pi^2 A}{h^2}\frac{\mu E_0}{2}c_{n,\,p}\cos\vartheta S_{n,\,p}.
\end{aligned}
\right\} \quad [171]
$$

We observe that $h^2/8\pi^2 A$ is the energy quantum formerly called u, and for $W_{n,\,p}$ we found the expression $n(n+1)u$; the quotient $\mu E_0/u$ we will call κ, as before in the case of the statical field, and finally the new quantity $h\nu/u$ characteristic for the impressed frequency will be called η. Instead of [171] we may then write

$$
\left.
\begin{aligned}
\nabla^2 g_1 + [n(n+1)+\eta]g_1 &= -\frac{\kappa}{2}c_{n,\,p}\cos\vartheta S_{n,\,p}, \\
\nabla^2 g_2 + [n(n+1)-\eta]g_2 &= -\frac{\kappa}{2}c_{n,\,p}\cos\vartheta S_{n,\,p}.
\end{aligned}
\right\} \quad [171']
$$

According to the first of the recurrence relations mentioned in the foregoing section, we have

$$
(2n+1)\cos\vartheta S_{n,\,p} = (n-p+1)S_{n+1,\,p} + (n+p)S_{n-1,\;p}.
$$

On the other hand $S_{n,\,p}$ is a solution of the equation [168], that is, if we apply the differentiation process indicated by ∇^2, the function itself is reproduced multiplied with the factor $-n(n+1)$. Keeping this in mind, it is easily seen that

$$
\left.
\begin{aligned}
g_1 &= -\frac{\kappa}{2}c_{n,\,p}\left[\frac{n-p+1}{2n+1}\frac{S_{n+1,\,p}}{-2(n+1)+\eta}\right. \\
&\qquad\qquad\qquad \left. + \frac{n+p}{2n+1}\frac{S_{n-1,\,p}}{2n+\eta}\right], \\
g_2 &= -\frac{\kappa}{2}c_{n,\,p}\left[\frac{n-p+1}{2n+1}\frac{S_{n+1,\,p}}{-2(n+1)-\eta}\right. \\
&\qquad\qquad\qquad \left. + \frac{n+p}{2n+1}\frac{S_{n-1,\,p}}{2n-\eta}\right].
\end{aligned}
\right\} \quad [172]
$$

If we substitute these functions for g_1 and g_2 in [170], we have found one of the wave functions for the disturbed system according to [167]. We will find all of them in substituting for n and p the whole numbers which they may assume.

32. Infra-red Dispersion of a Polar Gas.

As we considered the transition of a state n', p' to a state n, p in Section 30, we concluded that the radiation of this transition was equivalent to the classical radiation of the vibrating moments m_x,

m_y, m_z. In particular m_z was defined by the equation

$$m_z = \mu \int \int \cos \vartheta \overline{\Psi}_{n', p'} \Psi_{n, p} d\Omega \qquad [173]$$

as the moment vibrating in the direction of E_0. The frequency was

$$\nu = \frac{W_{n', p'} - W_{n, p}}{h}$$

and we calculated m_z in the limiting case $E_0 = 0$. It would have been possible to apply this calculation to the interaction of two wave functions of the same indices. The frequency would have been $\nu = 0$ and the result would have been an expression for the statical moment equivalent to the state n, p disturbed by a constant field. This is indeed another method to calculate the polarizability of the gas. We would only have had to take care not to introduce the limiting value of Ψ for $E = 0$, but the second approximation containing a term of the order E.

The same method can be applied in the present case to find the equivalent moment vibrating with the frequency ν of the disturbing field.

Let us first calculate the product $\Psi_{n, p} \overline{\Psi}_{n, p}$. If Ψ is given by [167] and G is defined by [170] and [171'], a simple calculation yields the expression

$$\Psi_{n, p} \overline{\Psi}_{n, p} = c_{n, p}^2 \left\{ S_{n, p}^2 - 2\kappa \cos 2\pi\nu t S_{n, p} \right.$$

$$\times \left[\frac{n - p + 1}{2n + 1} \frac{-2(n + 1)}{4(n + 1)^2 - \eta^2} S_{n+1, p} \qquad [174] \right.$$

$$\left. \left. + \frac{n + p}{2n + 1} \frac{2n}{4n^2 - \eta^2} S_{n-1, p} \right] \right\}.$$

The first thing to be done is to normalize the function Ψ. If we integrate [174] over the sphere, only the first term in the brackets is of importance, for the harmonics are orthogonal and we find for $c_{n, p}^2$ the values already mentioned in equations [162] and [162'] of Section 30. To evaluate the equivalent moment m_z we have to multiply the product $\Psi\overline{\Psi}$ with $\mu \cos \vartheta$ (see equation [173]) and to integrate again over the sphere. The recurrence relation

$$(2n + 1) \cos \vartheta S_{n, p} = (n - p + 1)S_{n+1, p} + (n + p)S_{n-1, p},$$

mentioned several times, shows that now the first term in the brackets gives zero. The second term leads to a finite value, the final result being [4]

$$m_z = -2\mu\kappa \cos 2\pi\nu t \left[\frac{(n+1)^2 - p^2}{(2n+1)(2n+3)} \frac{-2(n+1)}{4(n+1)^2 - \eta^2} \right. \\ \left. + \frac{n^2 - p^2}{(2n-1)(2n+1)} \frac{2n}{4n^2 - \eta^2} \right], \qquad [175]$$

where, as before, the numeric η stands for $h\nu/u$. We learn from equation [175] that a molecule in the state n, p disturbed by a periodic field of frequency ν is equivalent to a moment vibrating in the direction of the field with the same frequency. The amplitude of this moment becomes large (theoretically infinite if we apply [175], which however is not allowed) if

$$\nu = 2(n+1)\frac{u}{h} \qquad \text{or} \qquad \nu = 2n\frac{u}{h}.$$

Now a free molecule can have a transition from n to $n - 1$ and in this transition it will radiate energy of the frequency

$$\nu = [n(n+1) - n(n-1)]\frac{u}{h} = 2n\frac{u}{h}.$$

The other possible transition is from n to $n + 1$, in which it will absorb energy of the frequency

$$\nu = [(n+1)(n+2) - n(n+1)]\frac{u}{h} = 2(n+1)\frac{u}{h}.$$

We see that the amplitude of the moment has a close connection with the frequencies involved in these two transitions, which are moreover the only ones possible, as was shown in Section 30. In this way equation [175] gives an illustration of the principles on which Kramers [5] derived his dispersion formula and [175] is indeed his formula in which the coefficients have been definitely adapted to our special case. The difference in sign of the two terms differentiates also the absorption process from the emission process.

If now we have a polar gas of temperature T, the number of molecules with the rotational energy $n(n + 1)u$ is proportional to

$$(2n + 1)e^{-n(n+1)(u/kT)};$$

[4] The relation

$$\int \dot{S}_n{}^2 d\Omega = \begin{cases} \pi \dfrac{2}{2n+1} \dfrac{(n+p)!}{(n-p)!}; & p \neq 0 \\ 2\pi \dfrac{2}{2n+1}; & p = 0 \end{cases}$$

has to be used in this calculation.

[5] H. A. Kramers, *Nature*, **113**, 307 (1924); **114**, 310 (1924).

for the multiplicity of the level n is $2n + 1$. Every sublevel characterized by a value p will be present in a number of molecules proportional to

$$e^{-n(n+1)(u/kT)}$$

if we allow p to take all the values from $-n$ to $+n$. In order to compute the average moment $m_z{}^*$ of a molecule of the rotational energy $n(n + 1)u$, we have therefore to take the sum of the expression m_z over all the values of p going from $-n$ to $+n$ and to divide this by the number of sublevels $2n + 1$. Now using the relation

$$\sum_{-n}^{+n} p^2 = \tfrac{1}{3}n(n + 1)(2n + 1)$$

in performing the summation in [175], we will find for the average moment $m_z{}^*$ of a molecule in the state n the expression

$$m_z{}^* = \frac{1}{2n + 1}\,\frac{\mu\kappa}{3}\,\cos 2\pi\nu t\left[\frac{4(n + 1)^2}{4(n + 1)^2 - \eta^2} - \frac{4n^2}{4n^2 - \eta^2}\right]. \qquad [176]$$

For the special state $n = 0$, we have

$$m_z{}^* = \frac{\mu\kappa}{3}\,\cos 2\pi\nu t\,\frac{4}{4 - \eta^2}. \qquad [176']$$

According to what has been said concerning the number of molecules in the state n, we find for the average moment $\overline{m}_z$ of one molecule

$$\overline{m}_z = \frac{\mu\kappa}{3}\,\cos 2\pi\nu t$$

$$\times \frac{\dfrac{4}{4 - \eta^2} + \sum\limits_{n=1}^{\infty}\left[\dfrac{4(n + 1)^2}{4(n + 1)^2 - \eta^2} - \dfrac{4n^2}{4n^2 - \eta^2}\right]e^{-n(n+1)(u/kT)}}{\sum\limits_{n=0}^{\infty}(2n + 1)e^{-n(n+1)(u/kT)}}. \qquad [177]$$

In the special case $\nu = 0$ or $\eta = h\nu/u = 0$ the sum in the numerator vanishes and we have

$$\overline{m}_z = \frac{\mu\kappa}{3}\,\frac{1}{\sum\limits_{n=0}^{\infty}(2n + 1)e^{-n(n+1)(u/kT)}},$$

and this is, as it should be, the same value as was found by another method in Section 29 for the static field. In that section we introduced the temperature T_k characteristic for the molecule by the definition $u = kT_k$ and found that T_k is practically a small number

(14.7 for HCl).   Taking this into account, we could show that the sum in the denominator of [177] is nearly equal to kT/u.   We can of course characterize the molecule also by a characteristic frequency.   Letting $h\nu_k = u$, this frequency will be

$$\nu_k = \frac{\kappa}{h} T_k = 2.09 \times 10^{10} T_k$$

and for HCl is equal to 30.7×10^{10}; for gases with a larger moment of inertia A it will be smaller, as it is proportional to the reciprocal of A.   Our numeric η is $h\nu/u$, equal to ν/ν_k, while the numeric κ is $\mu E_0/u$.   The coefficient of $E_0 \cos 2\pi\nu t$ in [177] is the polarizability and with our former notation (r for the index of refractivity, M for the molecular weight, ρ for the density, P for the molar polarization, N for Avogadro's number) we can now transform [177] into the equation

$$
P = \frac{r^2 - 1}{3} \frac{M}{\rho} = \frac{4\pi N}{3} \frac{\mu^2}{3kT} \left\{ \frac{1}{1 - \left(\dfrac{\nu}{2\nu_k}\right)^2} \right.
$$
$$
+ \sum_{n=1}^{\infty} \left[\frac{1}{1 - \left(\dfrac{\nu}{2(n+1)\nu_k}\right)^2} \right.
$$
$$
\left. \left. - \frac{1}{1 - \left(\dfrac{\nu}{2n\nu_k}\right)^2} \right] \times e^{-n(n+1)(T_k/T)} \right\}, \qquad [178]
$$

which can also be given the form

$$
P = \frac{4\pi N}{3} \frac{\mu^2}{3kT} \sum_{n=1}^{\infty} \frac{1}{1 - \left(\dfrac{\nu}{2n\nu_k}\right)^2} \left[e^{-n(n-1)(T_k/T)} - e^{-n(n+1)(T_k/T)} \right]. \quad [178']
$$

The dispersion becomes large in the neighborhood of the lines $\nu = 2n\nu_k$, which are the absorption lines.   In HCl gas the first of these lines has the frequency $\nu = 2\nu_k = 61.4 \times 10^{10}$, or the wavelength 4.88×10^{-2} cm.   A moment of inertia 100 times as large as that of HCl would bring the wave-length to 4.88 cm. and would perhaps make it possible to detect a faint beginning of the corresponding dispersion in the range of radio frequencies.

The intensity of a dispersion line may be measured by the factor

$$
e^{-n(n-1)(T_k/T)} - e^{-n(n+1)(T_k/T)} = e^{-n^2(T_k/T)}\left(e^{n(T_k/T)} - e^{-n(T_k/T)}\right).
$$

With increasing index n this intensity first increases, reaches a maximum and afterwards fades away rapidly.   To discuss the first beginning of the dispersion for small frequencies, we may develop [178'] in powers of ν/ν_k. Retaining the first two terms of this development, we obtain for the molar polarization

$$P = \frac{4\pi N}{3}\frac{\mu^2}{3kT}\left\{1 + \frac{\nu^2}{2\nu_k^2}\sum_{n=1}^{\infty}\frac{e^{-n^2(T_k/T)}}{n^2} \times \sinh n\frac{T_k}{T}\right\}. \quad [179]$$

The coefficient of ν^2 is certainly positive; the molar polarization will therefore increase with increasing frequency and will reach a first positive infinite value for $\nu = 2\nu_k$, if we take [178'] literally. Therefore in gases we have the opposite of the effect in liquids, discussed in Chapter V, where anomalous dispersion, *i.e.*, a decrease of the dielectric constant with increasing frequency, is exhibited.

AUTHOR INDEX

SUBJECT INDEX

171

CATALOGUE OF DOVER BOOKS

PHYSICS

General physics

FOUNDATIONS OF PHYSICS, R. B. Lindsay & H. Margenau. Excellent bridge between semi-popular works & technical treatises. A discussion of methods of physical description, construction of theory; valuable for physicist with elementary calculus who is interested in ideas that give meaning to data, tools of modern physics. Contents include symbolism, mathematical equations; space & time foundations of mechanics; probability; physics & continua; electron theory; special & general relativity; quantum mechanics; causality. "Thorough and yet not overdetailed. Unreservedly recommended," NATURE (London). Unabridged, corrected edition. List of recommended readings. 35 illustrations. xi + 537pp. 5⅜ x 8.
S377 Paperbound **$2.75**

FUNDAMENTAL FORMULAS OF PHYSICS, ed. by D. H. Menzel. Highly useful, fully inexpensive reference and study text, ranging from simple to highly sophisticated operations. Mathematics integrated into text—each chapter stands as short textbook of field represented. Vol. 1: Statistics, Physical Constants, Special Theory of Relativity, Hydrodynamics, Aerodynamics, Boundary Value Problems in Math. Physics; Viscosity, Electromagnetic Theory, etc. Vol. 2: Sound, Acoustics, Geometrical Optics, Electron Optics, High-Energy Phenomena, Magnetism, Biophysics, much more. Index. Total of 800pp. 5⅜ x 8. Vol. 1 S595 Paperbound **$2.00**
Vol. 2 S596 Paperbound **$2.00**

MATHEMATICAL PHYSICS, D. H. Menzel. Thorough one-volume treatment of the mathematical techniques vital for classic mechanics, electromagnetic theory, quantum theory, and relativity. Written by the Harvard Professor of Astrophysics for junior, senior, and graduate courses, it gives clear explanations of all those aspects of function theory, vectors, matrices, dyadics, tensors, partial differential equations, etc., necessary for the understanding of the various physical theories. Electron theory, relativity, and other topics seldom presented appear here in considerable detail. Scores of definitions, conversion factors, dimensional constants, etc. "More detailed than normal for an advanced text . . . excellent set of sections on Dyadics, Matrices, and Tensors," JOURNAL OF THE FRANKLIN INSTITUTE. Index. 193 problems, with answers. x + 412pp. 5⅜ x 8. S56 Paperbound **$2.00**

THE SCIENTIFIC PAPERS OF J. WILLARD GIBBS. All the published papers of America's outstanding theoretical scientist (except for "Statistical Mechanics" and "Vector Analysis"). Vol I (thermodynamics) contains one of the most brilliant of all 19th-century scientific papers—the 300-page "On the Equilibrium of Heterogeneous Substances," which founded the science of physical chemistry, and clearly stated a number of highly important natural laws for the first time; 8 other papers complete the first volume. Vol II includes 2 papers on dynamics, 8 on vector analysis and multiple algebra, 5 on the electromagnetic theory of light, and 6 miscellaneous papers. Biographical sketch by H. A. Bumstead. Total of xxxvi + 718pp. 5⅝ x 8⅜.
S721 Vol I Paperbound **$2.50**
S722 Vol II Paperbound **$2.00**
The set **$4.50**

BASIC THEORIES OF PHYSICS, Peter Gabriel Bergmann. Two-volume set which presents a critical examination of important topics in the major subdivisions of classical and modern physics. The first volume is concerned with classical mechanics and electrodynamics: mechanics of mass points, analytical mechanics, matter in bulk, electrostatics and magnetostatics, electromagnetic interaction, the field waves, special relativity, and waves. The second volume (Heat and Quanta) contains discussions of the kinetic hypothesis, physics and statistics, stationary ensembles, laws of thermodynamics, early quantum theories, atomic spectra, probability waves, quantization in wave mechanics, approximation methods, and abstract quantum theory. A valuable supplement to any thorough course or text.
Heat and Quanta: Index. 8 figures. x + 300pp. 5⅜ x 8½. S968 Paperbound **$1.75**
Mechanics and Electrodynamics: Index. 14 figures. vii + 280pp. 5⅜ x 8½.
S969 Paperbound **$1.75**

THEORETICAL PHYSICS, A. S. Kompaneyets. One of the very few thorough studies of the subject in this price range. Provides advanced students with a comprehensive theoretical background. Especially strong on recent experimentation and developments in quantum theory. Contents: Mechanics (Generalized Coordinates, Lagrange's Equation, Collision of Particles, etc.), Electrodynamics (Vector Analysis, Maxwell's equations, Transmission of Signals, Theory of Relativity, etc.), Quantum Mechanics (the Inadequacy of Classical Mechanics, the Wave Equation, Motion in a Central Field, Quantum Theory of Radiation, Quantum Theories of Dispersion and Scattering, etc.), and Statistical Physics (Equilibrium Distribution of Molecules in an Ideal Gas, Boltzmann statistics, Bose and Fermi Distribution, Thermodynamic Quantities, etc.). Revised to 1961. Translated by George Yankovsky, authorized by Kompaneyets. 137 exercises. 56 figures. 529pp. 5⅜ x 8½. S972 Paperbound **$2.50**

ANALYTICAL AND CANONICAL FORMALISM IN PHYSICS, André Mercier. A survey, in one volume, of the variational principles (the key principles—in mathematical form—from which the basic laws of any one branch of physics can be derived) of the several branches of physical theory, together with an examination of the relationships among them. Contents: the Lagrangian Formalism, Lagrangian Densities, Canonical Formalism, Canonical Form of Electrodynamics, Hamiltonian Densities, Transformations, and Canonical Form with Vanishing Jacobian Determinant. Numerous examples and exercises. For advanced students, teachers, etc. 6 figures. Index. viii + 222pp. 5⅜ x 8½. S1077 Paperbound **$1.75**

Acoustics, optics, electricity and magnetism, electromagnetics, magneto-hydrodynamics

THE THEORY OF SOUND, Lord Rayleigh. Most vibrating systems likely to be encountered in practice can be tackled successfully by the methods set forth by the great Nobel laureate, Lord Rayleigh. Complete coverage of experimental, mathematical aspects of sound theory. Partial contents: Harmonic motions, vibrating systems in general, lateral vibrations of bars, curved plates or shells, applications of Laplace's functions to acoustical problems, fluid friction, plane vortex-sheet, vibrations of solid bodies, etc. This is the first inexpensive edition of this great reference and study work. Bibliography. Historical introduction by R. B. Lindsay. Total of 1040pp. 97 figures. 5⅜ x 8.
S292, S293, Two volume set, paperbound, **$4.70**

THE DYNAMICAL THEORY OF SOUND, H. Lamb. Comprehensive mathematical treatment of the physical aspects of sound, covering the theory of vibrations, the general theory of sound, and the equations of motion of strings, bars, membranes, pipes, and resonators. Includes chapters on plane, spherical, and simple harmonic waves, and the Helmholtz Theory of Audition. Complete and self-contained development for student and specialist; all fundamental differential equations solved completely. Specific mathematical details for such important phenomena as harmonics, normal modes, forced vibrations of strings, theory of reed pipes, etc. Index. Bibliography. 86 diagrams. viii + 307pp. 5⅜ x 8.
S655 Paperbound **$1.50**

WAVE PROPAGATION IN PERIODIC STRUCTURES, L. Brillouin. A general method and application to different problems: pure physics, such as scattering of X-rays of crystals, thermal vibration in crystal lattices, electronic motion in metals; and also problems of electrical engineering. Partial contents: elastic waves in 1-dimensional lattices of point masses. Propagation of waves along 1-dimensional lattices. Energy flow. 2 dimensional, 3 dimensional lattices. Mathieu's equation. Matrices and propagation of waves along an electric line. Continuous electric lines. 131 illustrations. Bibliography. Index. xii + 253pp. 5⅜ x 8.
S34 Paperbound **$2.00**

THEORY OF VIBRATIONS, N. W. McLachlan. Based on an exceptionally successful graduate course given at Brown University, this discusses linear systems having 1 degree of freedom, forced vibrations of simple linear systems, vibration of flexible strings, transverse vibrations of bars and tubes, transverse vibration of circular plate, sound waves of finite amplitude, etc. Index. 99 diagrams. 160pp. 5⅜ x 8.
S190 Paperbound **$1.35**

LIGHT: PRINCIPLES AND EXPERIMENTS, George S. Monk. Covers theory, experimentation, and research. Intended for students with some background in general physics and elementary calculus. Three main divisions: 1) Eight chapters on geometrical optics—fundamental concepts (the ray and its optical length, Fermat's principle, etc.), laws of image formation, apertures in optical systems, photometry, optical instruments etc.; 2) 9 chapters on physical optics—interference, diffraction, polarization, spectra, the Rayleigh refractometer, the wave theory of light, etc.; 3) 23 instructive experiments based directly on the theoretical text. "Probably the best intermediate textbook on light in the English language. Certainly, it is the best book which includes both geometrical and physical optics," J. Rud Nielson, PHYSICS FORUM. Revised edition. 102 problems and answers. 12 appendices. 6 tables. Index. 270 illustrations. xi +489pp. 5⅜ x 8½.
S341 Paperbound **$2.50**

PHOTOMETRY, John W. T. Walsh. The best treatment of both "bench" and "illumination" photometry in English by one of Britain's foremost experts in the field (President of the International Commission on Illumination). Limited to those matters, theoretical and practical, which affect the measurement of light flux, candlepower, illumination, etc., and excludes treatment of the use to which such measurements may be put after they have been made. Chapters on Radiation, The Eye and Vision, Photo-Electric Cells, The Principles of Photometry, The Measurement of Luminous Intensity, Colorimetry, Spectrophotometry, Stellar Photometry, The Photometric Laboratory, etc. Third revised (1958) edition. 281 illustrations. 10 appendices. xxiv + 544pp. 5½ x 9¼.
S319 Clothbound **$10.00**

EXPERIMENTAL SPECTROSCOPY, R. A. Sawyer. Clear discussion of prism and grating spectrographs and the techniques of their use in research, with emphasis on those principles and techniques that are fundamental to practically all uses of spectroscopic equipment. Beginning with a brief history of spectroscopy, the author covers such topics as light sources, spectroscopic apparatus, prism spectroscopes and graphs, diffraction grating, the photographic process, determination of wave length, spectral intensity, infrared spectroscopy, spectrochemical analysis, etc. This revised edition contains new material on the production of replica gratings, solar spectroscopy from rockets, new standard of wave length, etc. Index. Bibliography. 111 illustrations. x + 358pp. 5⅜ x 8½.
S1045 Paperbound **$2.25**

FUNDAMENTALS OF ELECTRICITY AND MAGNETISM, L. B. Loeb. For students of physics, chemistry, or engineering who want an introduction to electricity and magnetism on a higher level and in more detail than general elementary physics texts provide. Only elementary differential and integral calculus is assumed. Physical laws developed logically, from magnetism to electric currents, Ohm's law, electrolysis, and on to static electricity, induction, etc. Covers an unusual amount of material; one third of book on modern material: solution of wave equation, photoelectric and thermionic effects, etc. Complete statement of the various electrical systems of units and interrelations. 2 Indexes. 75 pages of problems with answers stated. Over 300 figures and diagrams. xix +669pp. 5⅜ x 8.
S745 Paperbound **$2.75**

MATHEMATICAL ANALYSIS OF ELECTRICAL AND OPTICAL WAVE-MOTION, Harry Bateman. Written by one of this century's most distinguished mathematical physicists, this is a practical introduction to those developments of Maxwell's electromagnetic theory which are directly connected with the solution of the partial differential equation of wave motion. Methods of solving wave-equation, polar-cylindrical coordinates, diffraction, transformation of coordinates, homogeneous solutions, electromagnetic fields with moving singularities, etc. Index. 168pp. 5⅜ x 8.   S14 Paperbound **$1.75**

PRINCIPLES OF PHYSICAL OPTICS, Ernst Mach. This classical examination of the propagation of light, color, polarization, etc. offers an historical and philosophical treatment that has never been surpassed for breadth and easy readability. Contents: Rectilinear propagation of light. Reflection, refraction. Early knowledge of vision. Dioptrics. Composition of light. Theory of color and dispersion. Periodicity. Theory of interference. Polarization. Mathematical representation of properties of light. Propagation of waves, etc. 279 illustrations, 10 portraits. Appendix. Indexes. 324pp. 5⅜ x 8.   S178 Paperbound **$2.00**

THE THEORY OF OPTICS, Paul Drude. One of finest fundamental texts in physical optics, classic offers thorough coverage, complete mathematical treatment of basic ideas. Includes fullest treatment of application of thermodynamics to optics; sine law in formation of images, transparent crystals, magnetically active substances, velocity of light, apertures, effects depending upon them, polarization, optical instruments, etc. Introduction by A. A. Michelson. Index. 110 illus. 567pp. 5⅜ x 8.   S532 Paperbound **$2.45**

ELECTRICAL THEORY ON THE GIORGI SYSTEM, P. Cornelius. A new clarification of the fundamental concepts of electricity and magnetism, advocating the convenient m.k.s. system of units that is steadily gaining followers in the sciences. Illustrating the use and effectiveness of his terminology with numerous applications to concrete technical problems, the author here expounds the famous Giorgi system of electrical physics. His lucid presentation and well-reasoned, cogent argument for the universal adoption of this system form one of the finest pieces of scientific exposition in recent years. 28 figures. Index. Conversion tables for translating earlier data into modern units. Translated from 3rd Dutch edition by L. J. Jolley. x + 187pp. 5½ x 8¾.   S909 Clothbound **$6.00**

ELECTRIC WAVES: BEING RESEARCHES ON THE PROPAGATION OF ELECTRIC ACTION WITH FINITE VELOCITY THROUGH SPACE, Heinrich Hertz. This classic work brings together the original papers in which Hertz—Helmholtz's protegé and one of the most brilliant figures in 19th-century research—probed the existence of electromagnetic waves and showed experimentally that their velocity equalled that of light, research that helped lay the groundwork for the development of radio, television, telephone, telegraph, and other modern technological marvels. Unabridged republication of original edition. Authorized translation by D. E. Jones. Preface by Lord Kelvin. Index of names. 40 illustrations. xvii + 278pp. 5⅜ x 8½.
S57 Paperbound **$1.75**

PIEZOELECTRICITY: AN INTRODUCTION TO THE THEORY AND APPLICATIONS OF ELECTRO-MECHANICAL PHENOMENA IN CRYSTALS, Walter G. Cady. This is the most complete and systematic coverage of this important field in print—now regarded as something of scientific classic. This republication, revised and corrected by Prof. Cady—one of the foremost contributors in this area—contains a sketch of recent progress and new material on Ferroelectrics. Time Standards, etc. The first 7 chapters deal with fundamental theory of crystal electricity. 5 important chapters cover basic concepts of piezoelectricity, including comparisons of various competing theories in the field. Also discussed: piezoelectric resonators (theory, methods of manufacture, influences of air-gaps, etc.); the piezo oscillator; the properties, history, and observations relating to Rochelle salt; ferroelectric crystals; miscellaneous applications of piezoelectricity; pyroelectricity; etc. "A great work," W. A. Wooster, NATURE. Revised (1963) and corrected edition. New preface by Prof. Cady. 2 Appendices. Indices. Illustrations. 62 tables. Bibliography. Problems. Total of 1 + 822pp. 5⅜ x 8½.
S1094 Vol. I Paperbound **$2.50**
S1095 Vol. II Paperbound **$2.50**
Two volume set Paperbound **$5.00**

MAGNETISM AND VERY LOW TEMPERATURES, H. B. G. Casimir. A basic work in the literature of low temperature physics. Presents a concise survey of fundamental theoretical principles, and also points out promising lines of investigation. Contents: Classical Theory and Experimental Methods, Quantum Theory of Paramagnetism, Experiments on Adiabatic Demagnetization. Theoretical Discussion of Paramagnetism at Very Low Temperatures, Some Experimental Results, Relaxation Phenomena. Index. 89-item bibliography. ix + 95pp. 5⅜ x 8.
S943 Paperbound **$1.25**

SELECTED PAPERS ON NEW TECHNIQUES FOR ENERGY CONVERSION: THERMOELECTRIC METHODS; THERMIONIC; PHOTOVOLTAIC AND ELECTRICAL EFFECTS; FUSION, Edited by Sumner N. Levine. Brings together in one volume the most important papers (1954-1961) in modern energy technology. Included among the 37 papers are general and qualitative descriptions of the field as a whole, indicating promising lines of research. Also: 15 papers on thermoelectric methods, 7 on thermionic, 5 on photovoltaic, 4 on electrochemical effect, and 2 on controlled fusion research. Among the contributors are: Joffe, Maria Telkes, Herold, Herring, Douglas, Jaumot, Post, Austin, Wilson, Pfann, Rappaport, Morehouse, Domenicali, Moss, Bowers, Harman, Von Doenhoef. Preface and introduction by the editor. Bibliographies. xxviii + 451pp. 6⅛ x 9¼.   S37 Paperbound **$3.00**

ENGINEERING AND TECHNOLOGY

General and mathematical

ENGINEERING MATHEMATICS, Kenneth S. Miller. A text for graduate students of engineering to strengthen their mathematical background in differential equations, etc. Mathematical steps very explicitly indicated. Contents: Determinants and Matrices, Integrals, Linear Differential Equations, Fourier Series and Integrals, Laplace Transform, Network Theory, Random Function . . . all vital requisites for advanced modern engineering studies. Unabridged republication. Appendices: Borel Sets; Riemann-Stieltjes Integral; Fourier Series and Integrals. Index. References at Chapter Ends. xii + 417pp. 6 x 8½. **S1121 Paperbound $2.00**

MATHEMATICAL ENGINEERING ANALYSIS, Rufus Oldenburger. A book designed to assist the research engineer and scientist in making the transition from physical engineering situations to the corresponding mathematics. Scores of common practical situations found in all major fields of physics are supplied with their correct mathematical formulations—applications to automobile springs and shock absorbers, clocks, throttle torque of diesel engines, resistance networks, capacitors, transmission lines, microphones, neon tubes, gasoline engines, refrigeration cycles, etc. Each section reviews basic principles of underlying various fields: mechanics of rigid bodies, electricity and magnetism, heat, elasticity, fluid mechanics, and aerodynamics. Comprehensive and eminently useful. Index. 169 problems, answers. 200 photos and diagrams. xiv + 426pp. 5⅜ x 8½. **S919 Paperbound $2.00**

MATHEMATICS OF MODERN ENGINEERING, E. G. Keller and R. E. Doherty. Written for the Advanced Course in Engineering of the General Electric Corporation, deals with the engineering use of determinants, tensors, the Heaviside operational calculus, dyadics, the calculus of variations, etc. Presents underlying principles fully, but purpose is to teach engineers to deal with modern engineering problems, and emphasis is on the perennial engineering attack of set-up and solve. Indexes. Over 185 figures and tables. Hundreds of exercises, problems, and worked-out examples. References. Two volume set. Total of xxxiii + 623pp. 5⅜ x 8.
S734 Vol I Paperbound **$1.85**
S735 Vol II Paperbound **$1.85**
The set **$3.70**

MATHEMATICAL METHODS FOR SCIENTISTS AND ENGINEERS, L. P. Smith. For scientists and engineers, as well as advanced math students. Full investigation of methods and practical description of conditions under which each should be used. Elements of real functions, differential and integral calculus, space geometry, theory of residues, vector and tensor analysis, series of Bessel functions, etc. Each method illustrated by completely-worked-out examples, mostly from scientific literature. 368 graded unsolved problems. 100 diagrams. x + 453pp. 5⅝ x 8⅜. **S220 Paperbound $2.00**

THEORY OF FUNCTIONS AS APPLIED TO ENGINEERING PROBLEMS, edited by R. Rothe, F. Ollendorff, and K. Pohlhausen. A series of lectures given at the Berlin Institute of Technology that shows the specific applications of function theory in electrical and allied fields of engineering. Six lectures provide the elements of function theory in a simple and practical form, covering complex quantities and variables, integration in the complex plane, residue theorems, etc. Then 5 lectures show the exact uses of this powerful mathematical tool, with full discussions of problem methods. Index. Bibliography. 108 figures. x + 189pp. 5⅜ x 8.
S733 Paperbound $1.35

Aerodynamics and hydrodynamics

AIRPLANE STRUCTURAL ANALYSIS AND DESIGN, E. E. Sechler and L. G. Dunn. Systematic authoritative book which summarizes a large amount of theoretical and experimental work on structural analysis and design. Strong on classical subsonic material still basic to much aeronautic design . . . remains a highly useful source of information. Covers such areas as layout of the airplane, applied and design loads, stress-strain relationships for stable structures, truss and frame analysis, the problem of instability, the ultimate strength of stiffened flat sheet, analysis of cylindrical structures, wings and control surfaces, fuselage analysis, engine mounts, landing gears, etc. Originally published as part of the CALCIT Aeronautical Series. 256 Illustrations. 47 study problems. Indexes. xi + 420pp. 5⅜ x 8½.
S1043 Paperbound $2.25

FUNDAMENTALS OF HYDRO- AND AEROMECHANICS, L. Prandtl and O. G. Tietjens. The well-known standard work based upon Prandtl's lectures at Goettingen. Wherever possible hydrodynamics theory is referred to practical considerations in hydraulics, with the view of unifying theory and experience. Presentation is extremely clear and though primarily physical, mathematical proofs are rigorous and use vector analysis to a considerable extent. An Enginering Society Monograph, 1934. 186 figures. Index. xvi + 270pp. 5⅜ x 8.
S374 Paperbound $1.85

FLUID MECHANICS THROUGH WORKED EXAMPLES, D. R. L. Smith and J. Houghton. Advanced text covering principles and applications to practical situations. Each chapter begins with concise summaries of fundamental ideas. 163 fully worked out examples applying principles outlined in the text. 275 other problems, with answers. Contents: The Pressure of Liquids on Surfaces; Floating Bodies; Flow Under Constant Head in Pipes; Circulation; Vorticity; The Potential Function; Laminar Flow and Lubrication; Impact of Jets; Hydraulic Turbines; Centrifugal and Reciprocating Pumps; Compressible Fluids; and many other items. Total of 438 examples. 250 line illustrations. 340pp. Index. 6 x 8⅞. S981 Clothbound **$6.00**

THEORY OF SHIP MOTIONS, S. N. Blagoveshchensky. The only detailed text in English in a rapidly developing branch of engineering and physics, it is the work of one of the world's foremost authorities—Blagoveshchensky of Leningrad Shipbuilding Institute. A senior-level treatment written primarily for engineering students, but also of great importance to naval architects, designers, contractors, researchers in hydrodynamics, and other students. No mathematics beyond ordinary differential equations is required for understanding the text. Translated by T. & L. Strelkoff, under editorship of Louis Landweber, Iowa Institute of Hydraulic Research, under auspices of Office of Naval Research. Bibliography. Index. 231 diagrams and illustrations. Total of 649pp. 5⅜ x 8½. Vol. I: S234 Paperbound **$2.00** Vol. II: S235 Paperbound **$2.00**

THEORY OF FLIGHT, Richard von Mises. Remains almost unsurpassed as balanced, well-written account of fundamental fluid dynamics, and situations in which air compressibility effects are unimportant. Stressing equally theory and practice, avoiding formidable mathematical structure, it conveys a full understanding of physical phenomena and mathematical concepts. Contains perhaps the best introduction to general theory of stability. "Outstanding," Scientific, Medical, and Technical Books. New introduction by K. H. Hohenemser. Bibliographical, historical notes. Index. 408 illustrations. xvi + 620pp. 5⅜ x 8⅜. S541 Paperbound **$2.95**

THEORY OF WING SECTIONS, I. H. Abbott, A. E. von Doenhoff. Concise compilation of subsonic aerodynamic characteristics of modern NASA wing sections, with description of their geometry, associated theory. Primarily reference work for engineers, students, it gives methods, data for using wing-section data to predict characteristics. Particularly valuable: chapters on thin wings, airfoils; complete summary of NACA's experimental observations, system of construction families of airfoils. 350pp. of tables on Basic Thickness Forms, Mean Lines, Airfoil Ordinates, Aerodynamic Characteristics of Wing Sections. Index. Bibliography. 191 illustrations. Appendix. 705pp. 5⅜ x 8. S558 Paperbound **$3.25**

WEIGHT-STRENGTH ANALYSIS OF AIRCRAFT STRUCTURES, F. R. Shanley. Scientifically sound methods of analyzing and predicting the structural weight of aircraft and missiles. Deals directly with forces and the distances over which they must be transmitted, making it possible to develop methods by which the minimum structural weight can be determined for any material and conditions of loading. Weight equations for wing and fuselage structures. Includes author's original papers on inelastic buckling and creep buckling. "Particularly successful in presenting his analytical methods for investigating various optimum design principles," AERONAUTICAL ENGINEERING REVIEW. Enlarged bibliography. Index. 199 figures. xiv + 404pp. 5⅝ x 8⅜. S660 Paperbound **$2.45**

Electricity

TWO-DIMENSIONAL FIELDS IN ELECTRICAL ENGINEERING, L. V. Bewley. A useful selection of typical engineering problems of interest to practicing electrical engineers. Introduces senior students to the methods and procedures of mathematical physics. Discusses theory of functions of a complex variable, two-dimensional fields of flow, general theorems of mathematical physics and their applications, conformal mapping or transformation, method of images, freehand flux plotting, etc. New preface by the author. Appendix by W. F. Kiltner. Index. Bibliography at chapter ends. xiv + 204pp. 5⅜ x 8½. S1118 Paperbound **$1.50**

FLUX LINKAGES AND ELECTROMAGNETIC INDUCTION, L. V. Bewley. A brief, clear book which shows proper uses and corrects misconceptions of Faraday's law of electromagnetic induction in specific problems. Contents: Circuits; Turns, and Flux Linkages; Substitution of Circuits; Electromagnetic Induction; General Criteria for Electromagnetic Induction; Applications and Paradoxes; Theorem of Constant Flux Linkages. New Section: Rectangular Coil in a Varying Uniform Medium. Valuable supplement to class texts for engineering students. Corrected, enlarged edition. New preface. Bibliography in notes. 49 figures. xi + 106pp. 5⅜ x 8. S1103 Paperbound **$1.25**

INDUCTANCE CALCULATIONS: WORKING FORMULAS AND TABLES, Frederick W. Grover. An invaluable book to everyone in electrical engineering. Provides simple single formulas to cover all the more important cases of inductance. The approach involves only those parameters that naturally enter into each situation, while extensive tables are given to permit easy interpolations. Will save the engineer and student countless hours and enable them to obtain accurate answers with minimal effort. Corrected republication of 1946 edition. 58 tables. 97 completely worked out examples. 66 figures. xiv + 286pp. 5⅜ x 8½. S974 Paperbound **$1.85**

GASEOUS CONDUCTORS: THEORY AND ENGINEERING APPLICATIONS, J. D. Cobine. An indispensable text and reference to gaseous conduction phenomena, with the engineering viewpoint prevailing throughout. Studies the kinetic theory of gases, ionization, emission phenomena; gas breakdown, spark characteristics, glow, and discharges; engineering applications in circuit interrupters, rectifiers, light sources, etc. Separate detailed treatment of high pressure arcs (Suits); low pressure arcs (Langmuir and Tonks). Much more. "Well organized, clear, straightforward," Tonks, Review of Scientific Instruments. Index. Bibliography. 83 practice problems. 7 appendices. Over 600 figures. 58 tables. xx + 606pp. 5⅜ x 8. S442 Paperbound **$2.95**

INTRODUCTION TO THE STATISTICAL DYNAMICS OF AUTOMATIC CONTROL SYSTEMS, V. V. Solodovnikov. First English publication on important branch of automatic control systems—random signals; in its original edition, this was the first comprehensive treatment. Examines frequency characteristics, transfer functions, stationary random processes, determination of minimum mean-squared error, of transfer function for a finite period of observation, much more. Translation edited by J. B. Thomas, L. A. Zadeh. Index. Bibliography. Appendix. xxii + 308pp. 5⅜ x 8. S420 Paperbound **$2.25**

TENSORS FOR CIRCUITS, Gabriel Kron. A boldly original method of analyzing engineering problems, at center of sharp discussion since first introduced, now definitely proved useful in such areas as electrical and structural networks on automatic computers. Encompasses a great variety of specific problems by means of a relatively few symbolic equations. "Power and flexibility . . . becoming more widely recognized," Nature. Formerly "A Short Course in Tensor Analysis." New introduction by B. Hoffmann. Index. Over 800 diagrams. xix + 250pp. 5⅜ x 8. S534 Paperbound **$2.00**

SELECTED PAPERS ON SEMICONDUCTOR MICROWAVE ELECTRONICS, edited by Sumner N. Levine and Richard R. Kurzrok. An invaluable collection of important papers dealing with one of the most remarkable developments in solid-state electronics—the use of the **p-n** junction to achieve amplification and frequency conversion of microwave frequencies. Contents: General Survey (3 introductory papers by W. E. Danielson, R. N. Hall, and M. Tenzer); General Theory of Nonlinear Elements (3 articles by A. van der Ziel, H. E. Rowe, and Manley and Rowe); Device Fabrication and Characterization (3 pieces by Bakanowski, Cranna, and Uhlir, by McCotter, Walker and Fortini, and by S. T. Eng); Parametric Amplifiers and Frequency Multipliers (13 articles by Uhlir, Heffner and Wade, Matthaei, P. K. Tien, van der Ziel, Engelbrecht, Currie and Gould, Uenohara, Leeson and Weinreb, and others); and Tunnel Diodes (4 papers by L. Esaki, H. S. Sommers, Jr., M. E. Hines, and Yariv and Cook). Introduction. 295 Figures. xiii + 286pp. 6½ x 9¼. S1126 Paperbound **$2.25**

THE PRINCIPLES OF ELECTROMAGNETISM APPLIED TO ELECTRICAL MACHINES, B. Hague. A concise, but complete, summary of the basic principles of the magnetic field and its applications, with particular reference to the kind of phenomena which occur in electrical machines. Part I: General Theory—magnetic field of a current, electromagnetic field passing from air to iron, mechanical forces on linear conductors, etc. Part II: Application of theory to the solution of electromechanical problems—the magnetic field and mechanical forces in non-salient pole machinery, the field within slots and between salient poles, and the work of Rogowski, Roth, and Strutt. Formerly titled "Electromagnetic Problems in Electrical Engineering." 2 appendices. Index. Bibliography in notes. 115 figures. xiv + 359pp. 5⅜ x 8½. S246 Paperbound **$2.25**

Mechanical engineering

DESIGN AND USE OF INSTRUMENTS AND ACCURATE MECHANISM, T. N. Whitehead. For the instrument designer, engineer; how to combine necessary mathematical abstractions with independent observation of actual facts. Partial contents: instruments & their parts, theory of errors, systematic errors, probability, short period errors, erratic errors, design precision, kinematic, semikinematic design, stiffness, planning of an instrument, human factor, etc. Index. 85 photos, diagrams. xii + 288pp. 5⅜ x 8. S270 Paperbound **$2.00**

A TREATISE ON GYROSTATICS AND ROTATIONAL MOTION: THEORY AND APPLICATIONS, Andrew Gray. Most detailed, thorough book in English, generally considered definitive study. Many problems of all sorts in full detail, or step-by-step summary. Classical problems of Bour, Lottner, etc.; later ones of great physical interest. Vibrating systems of gyrostats, earth as a top, calculation of path of axis of a top by elliptic integrals, motion of unsymmetrical top, much more. Index. 160 illus. 550pp. 5⅜ x 8. S589 Paperbound **$2.75**

MECHANICS OF THE GYROSCOPE, THE DYNAMICS OF ROTATION, R. F. Deimel, Professor of Mechanical Engineering at Stevens Institute of Technology. Elementary general treatment of dynamics of rotation, with special application of gyroscopic phenomena. No knowledge of vectors needed. Velocity of a moving curve, acceleration to a point, general equations of motion, gyroscopic horizon, free gyro, motion of discs, the damped gyro, 103 similar topics. Exercises. 75 figures. 208pp. 5⅜ x 8. S66 Paperbound **$1.75**

PHILOSOPHY OF SCIENCE AND MATHEMATICS

FOUNDATIONS OF SCIENCE: THE PHILOSOPHY OF THEORY AND EXPERIMENT, N. R. Campbell.
A critique of the most fundamental concepts of science in general and physics in particular.
Examines why certain propositions are accepted without question, demarcates science from
philosophy, clarifies the understanding of the tools of science. Part One analyzes the pre-
suppositions of scientific thought: existence of the material world, nature of scientific
laws, multiplication of probabilities, etc.: Part Two covers the nature of experiment and the
application of mathematics: conditions for measurement, relations between numerical laws
and theories, laws of error, etc. An appendix covers problems arising from relativity, force,
motion, space, and time. A classic in its field. Index. xiii + 565pp. 5⅝ x 8⅜.
S372 Paperbound **$2.95**

THE NATURE OF PHYSICAL THEORY, P. W. Bridgman. Here is how modern physics looks to a
highly unorthodox physicist—a Nobel laureate. Pointing out many absurdities of science, and
demonstrating the inadequacies of various physical theories, Dr. Bridgman weighs and analyzes the contributions of Einstein, Bohr, Newton, Heisenberg, and many others. This is a
non-technical consideration of the correlation of science and reality. Index. xi + 138pp.
5⅜ x 8. S33 Paperbound **$1.25**

THE VALUE OF SCIENCE, Henri Poincaré. Many of the most mature ideas of the "last scientific
universalist" covered with charm and vigor for both the beginning student and the advanced
worker. Discusses the nature of scientific truth, whether order is innate in the universe
or imposed upon it by man, logical thought versus intuition (relating to math, through the
works of Weierstrass, Lie, Klein, Riemann), time and space (relativity, psychological time,
simultaneity), Hertz's concept of force, interrelationship of mathematical physics to pure
math, values within disciplines of Maxwell, Carnot, Mayer, Newton, Lorentz, etc. Index.
iii + 147pp. 5⅜ x 8. S469 Paperbound **$1.35**

SCIENCE AND HYPOTHESIS, Henri Poincaré. Creative psychology in science. How such concepts as number, magnitude, space, force, classical mechanics were developed, and how the
modern scientist uses them in his thought. Hypothesis in physics, theories of modern
physics. Introduction by Sir James Larmor. "Few mathematicians have had the breadth of
vision of Poincaré, and none is his superior in the gift of clear exposition," E. T. Bell.
Index. 272pp. 5⅜ x 8. S221 Paperbound **$1.35**

PHILOSOPHY AND THE PHYSICISTS, L. S. Stebbing. The philosophical aspects of modern
science examined in terms of a lively critical attack on the ideas of Jeans and Eddington.
Discusses the task of science, causality, determinism, probability, consciousness, the relation
of the world of physics to that of everyday experience. Probes the philosophical significance
of the Planck-Bohr concept of discontinuous energy levels, the inferences to be drawn from
Heisenberg's Uncertainty Principle, the implications of "becoming" involved in the 2nd law
of thermodynamics, and other problems posed by the discarding of Laplacean determinism.
285pp. 5⅜ x 8. T480 Paperbound **$1.65**

THE PHILOSOPHICAL WRITINGS OF PEIRCE, edited by Justus Buchler. (Formerly published as
THE PHILOSOPHY OF PEIRCE.) This is a carefully balanced exposition of Peirce's complete
system, written by Peirce himself. It covers such matters as scientific method, pure chance
vs. law, symbolic logic, theory of signs, pragmatism, experiment, and other topics. Introduction by Justus Buchler, Columbia University. xvi + 368pp. 5⅜ x 8.
T217 Paperbound **$2.00**

LANGUAGE, TRUTH AND LOGIC, A. Ayer. A clear introduction to the Vienna and Cambridge
schools of Logical Positivism. It sets up specific tests by which you can evaluate validity of
ideas, etc. Contents: Function of philosophy, elimination of metaphysics, nature of analysis,
a priori, truth and probability, etc. 10th printing. "I should like to have written it myself,"
Bertrand Russell. Index. 160pp. 5⅜ x 8. T10 Paperbound **$1.25**

**MATHEMATICS AND SCIENCE: LAST ESSAYS (DERNIÈRES PENSÉES), Henri Poincaré. Translated
by J. W. Bolduc.** A posthumous volume of articles and lectures by the great French mathe-
matician, philosopher, scientist. Here are nine pieces, never before translated into English,
on such subjects as The Evolution of Laws, Space and Time, Space and 3 Dimensions, The
Logic of infinity in Mathematics (discussing Russell's theory of types), Mathematics and Logic,
The Quantum Theory and its Modern Applications, Relationship Between Matter and Ether,
Ethics and Science and The Moral Alliance. First English translation of Dernières Pensées.
New index. viii + 128pp. 5⅜ x 8½. S1101 Paperbound **$1.25**

THE PSYCHOLOGY OF INVENTION IN THE MATHEMATICAL FIELD, J. Hadamard. Where do ideas
come from? What role does the unconscious play? Are ideas best developed by mathematical
reasoning, word reasoning, visualization? What are the methods used by Einstein, Poincaré,
Galton, Riemann? How can these techniques be applied by others? Hadamard, one of the
world's leading mathematicians, discusses these and other questions. xiii + 145pp. 5⅜ x 8.
T107 Paperbound **$1.25**

EXPERIMENT AND THEORY IN PHYSICS, Max Born. A Nobel laureate examines the nature and value of the counterclaims of experiment and theory in physics. Synthetic versus analytical scientific advances are analyzed in the work of Einstein, Bohr, Heisenberg, Planck, Eddington, Milne, and others by a fellow participant. 44pp. 5⅜ x 8.   S308 Paperbound 75¢

THE PHILOSOPHY OF SPACE AND TIME, H. Reichenbach. An important landmark in the development of the empiricist conception of geometry, covering the problem of the foundations of geometry, the theory of time, the consequences of Einstein's relativity, including: relations between theory and observations; coordinate and metrical properties of space; the psychological problem of visual intuition of non-Euclidean structures; and many other important topics in modern science and philosophy. The majority of ideas require only a knowledge of intermediate math. Introduction by R. Carnap. 49 figures. Index. xviii + 296pp. 5⅜ x 8.
S443 Paperbound **$2.00**

OBSERVATION AND INTERPRETATION IN THE PHILOSOPHY OF PHYSICS: WITH SPECIAL REFERENCE TO QUANTUM MECHANICS, Edited by S. Körner. A collection of papers by philosophers and physicists arising out of a symposium held at Bristol, England in 1957 under the auspices of the Colston Research Society. One of the most important contributions to the philosophy of science in recent years. The discussions center around the adequacy or inadequacy of quantum mechanics in its orthodox formulations. Among the contributors are A. J. Ayer, D. Bohm, K. Popper, F. Bopp, S. Körner, J. P. Vigier, M. Polanyi, P. K. Feyerabend, W. C. Kneale, W. B. Gallie, G. Ryle, Sir Charles Darwin, and R. B. Braithwaite. xiv + 218pp. 5⅜ x 8½.
S131 Paperbound **$1.60**

SPACE AND TIME IN CONTEMPORARY PHYSICS: AN INTRODUCTION TO THE THEORY OF RELATIVITY AND GRAVITATION, Moritz Schlick. Exposition of the theory of relativity by the leader of the famed "Vienna Circle." Its essential purpose is to describe the physical doctrines of special and general relativity with particular reference to their philosophical significance. Explanations of such topics as the geometrical relativity of space, the connection with inertia and gravitation, the measure-determination of the space-time continuum, the finite universe, etc., with their philosophical ramifications. Index. xii + 89pp. 5⅜ x 8½.
T1008 Paperbound **$1.00**

SUBSTANCE AND FUNCTION, & EINSTEIN'S THEORY OF RELATIVITY, Ernst Cassirer. Two books bound as one. Cassirer establishes a philosophy of the exact sciences that takes into consideration newer developments in mathematics, and also shows historical connections. Partial contents: Aristotelian logic, Mill's analysis, Helmholtz & Kronecker, Russell & cardinal numbers, Euclidean vs. non-Euclidean geometry, Einstein's relativity. Bibliography. Index. xxi + 465pp. 5⅜ x 8.
T50 Paperbound **$2.25**

PRINCIPLES OF MECHANICS, Heinrich Hertz. This last work by the great 19th century physicist is not only a classic, but of great interest in the logic of science. Creating a new system of mechanics based upon space, time, and mass, it returns to axiomatic analysis, to understanding of the formal or structural aspects of science, taking into account logic, observation, and a priori elements. Of great historical importance to Poincaré, Carnap, Einstein, Milne. A 20-page introduction by R. S. Cohen, Wesleyan University, analyzes the implications of Hertz's thought and the logic of science. Bibliography. 13-page introduction by Helmholtz. xlii + 274pp. 5⅜ x 8.
S316 Clothbound **$3.50**
S317 Paperbound **$1.85**

THE ANALYSIS OF MATTER, Bertrand Russell. How do our senses concord with the new physics? This volume covers such topics as logical analysis of physics, prerelativity physics, causality, scientific inference, physics and perception, special and general relativity, Weyl's theory, tensors, invariants and their physical interpretation, periodicity and qualitative series. "The most thorough treatment of the subject that has yet been published," THE NATION. Introduction by L. E. Denonn. 422pp. 5⅜ x 8.   T231 Paperbound **$1.95**

FOUNDATIONS OF GEOMETRY, Bertrand Russell. Analyzing basic problems in the overlap area between mathematics and philosophy, Nobel laureate Russell examines the nature of geometrical knowledge, the nature of geometry, and the application of geometry to space. It covers the history of non-Euclidean geometry, philosophic interpretations of geometry—especially Kant—projective and metrical geometry. This is most interesting as the solution offered in 1897 by a great mind to a problem still current. New introduction by Prof. Morris Kline of N. Y. University. xii + 201pp. 5⅜ x 8.   S232 Clothbound **$3.25**
S233 Paperbound **$1.75**

IDENTITY AND REALITY, Emile Meyerson. Called by Einstein a "brilliant study in the theory of knowledge," this book by the renowned Franco-German thinker is a major treatise in the philosophy of science and epistemology. Thorough, critical inquiries into causality, scientific laws, conservation of matter and energy, the unity of matter, Carnot's principle, the irrational, the elimination of time. Searches out the solutions of epistemological questions that form the bases of the scientific method. Authorized translation by Kate Loewenberg. Author's prefaces. Editor's preface. Appendices. Index. 495pp. 5⅜ x 8½.
T65 Paperbound **$2.25**

ESSAYS IN EXPERIMENTAL LOGIC, John Dewey. This stimulating series of essays touches upon the relationship between inquiry and experience, dependence of knowledge upon thought, character of logic; judgments of practice, data and meanings, stimuli of thought, etc. Index. viii + 444pp. 5⅜ x 8.   T73 Paperbound **$1.95**

MATHEMATICS, ELEMENTARY TO INTERMEDIATE

HOW TO CALCULATE QUICKLY, Henry Sticker. This handy volume offers a tried and true method for helping you in the basic mathematics of daily life—addition, subtraction, multiplication, division, fractions, etc. It is designed to awaken your "number sense" or the ability to see relationships between numbers as whole quantities. It is not a collection of tricks working only on special numbers, but a serious course of over 9,000 problems and their solutions, teaching special techniques not taught in schools: left-to-right multiplication, new fast ways of division, etc. 5 or 10 minutes daily use will double or triple your calculation speed. Excellent for the scientific worker who is at home in higher math, but is not satisfied with his speed and accuracy in lower mathematics. 256pp. 5 x 7¼.   T295 Paperbound **$1.00**

TEACH YOURSELF books. For adult self-study, for refresher and supplementary study.

The most effective series of home study mathematics books on the market! With absolutely no outside help, they will teach you as much as any similar college or high-school course, or will helpfully supplement any such course. Each step leads directly to the next, each question is anticipated. Numerous lucid examples and carefully-wrought practice problems illustrate meanings. Not skimpy outlines, not surveys, not usual classroom texts, these 204- to 380-page books are packed with the finest instruction you'll find anywhere for adult self-study.

TEACH YOURSELF ALGEBRA, P. Abbott. Formulas, coordinates, factors, graphs of quadratic functions, quadratic equations, logarithms, ratio, irrational numbers, arithmetical, geometrical series, much more. 1241 problems, solutions. Tables. 52 illus. 307pp. 6⅞ x 4¼.
Clothbound **$2.00**

TEACH YOURSELF GEOMETRY, P. Abbott. Solids, lines, points, surfaces, angle measurement, triangles, theorem of Pythagoras, polygons, loci, the circle, tangents, symmetry, solid geometry, prisms, pyramids, solids of revolution, etc. 343 problems, solutions. 268 illus. 334pp. 6⅞ x 4¼.
Clothbound **$2.00**

TEACH YOURSELF TRIGONOMETRY, P. Abbott. Geometrical foundations, indices, logarithms, trigonometrical ratios, relations between sides, angles of triangle, circular measure, trig. ratios of angles of any magnitude, much more. Requires elementary algebra, geometry. 465 problems, solutions. Tables. 102 illus. 204pp. 6⅞ x 4¼.   Clothbound **$2.00**

TEACH YOURSELF THE CALCULUS, P. Abbott. Variations in functions, differentiation, solids of revolution, series, elementary differential equations, areas by integral calculus, much more. Requires algebra, trigonometry. 970 problems, solutions. Tables. 89 illus. 380pp. 6⅞ x 4¼.
Clothbound **$2.00**

TEACH YOURSELF THE SLIDE RULE, B. Snodgrass. Fractions, decimals, A-D scales, log-log scales, trigonometrical scales, indices, logarithms. Commercial, precision, electrical, dualistic, Brighton rules. 80 problems, solutions. 10 illus. 207pp. 6⅞ x 4¼.   Clothbound **$2.00**

ARITHMETICAL EXCURSIONS: AN ENRICHMENT OF ELEMENTARY MATHEMATICS, H. Bowers and J. Bowers. For students who want unusual methods of arithmetic never taught in school; for adults who want to increase their number sense. Little known facts about the most simple numbers, arithmetical entertainments and puzzles, figurate numbers, number chains, mysteries and folklore of numbers, the "Hin-dog-abic" number system, etc. First publication. 50 figures. xiv + 320pp. 5⅜ x 8.   T770 Paperbound **$1.65**

HOW DO YOU USE A SLIDE RULE? by A. A. Merrill. Not a manual for mathematicians and engineers, but a lucid step-by-step explanation that presents the fundamental rules clearly enough to be understood by anyone who could benefit by the use of a slide rule in his work or business. This work concentrates on the 2 most important operations: multiplication and division. 10 easy lessons, each with a clear drawing, will save you countless hours in your banking, business, statistical, and other work. First publication. Index. 2 Appendixes. 10 illustrations. 78 problems, all with answers. vi + 36pp. 6⅛ x 9¼.   T62 Paperbound **60¢**

THE THEORY AND OPERATION OF THE SLIDE RULE, J. P. Ellis. Not a skimpy "instruction manual", but an exhaustive treatment that will save you hours throughout your career. Supplies full understanding of every scale on the Log Log Duplex Decitrig type of slide rule. Shows the most time-saving methods, and provides practice useful in the widest variety of actual engineering situations. Each operation introduced in terms of underlying logarithmic theory. Summary of prerequisite math. First publication. Index. 198 figures. Over 450 problems with answers. Bibliography. 12 Appendices. ix + 289pp. 5⅜ x 8.
S727 Paperbound **$1.50**

COLLEGE ALGEBRA, H. B. Fine. Standard college text that gives a systematic and deductive structure to algebra; comprehensive, connected, with emphasis on theory. Discusses the commutative, associative, and distributive laws of number in unusual detail, and goes on with undetermined coefficients, quadratic equations, progressions, logarithms, permutations, probability, power series, and much more. Still most valuable elementary-intermediate text on the science and structure of algebra. Index. 1560 problems, all with answers. x + 631pp. 5⅜ x 8. **T211 Paperbound $2.25**

COORDINATE GEOMETRY, L. P. Eisenhart. Thorough, unified introduction. Unusual for advancing in dimension within each topic (treats together circle, sphere; polar coordinates, 3-dimensional coordinate systems; conic sections, quadric surfaces), affording exceptional insight into subject. Extensive use made of determinants, though no previous knowledge of them is assumed. Algebraic equations of 1st degree, 2 and 3 unknowns, carried further than usual in algebra courses. Over 500 exercises. Introduction. Appendix. Index. Bibliography. 43 illustrations. 310pp. 5⅜ x 8. **S600 Paperbound $1.65**

A TREATISE ON PLANE AND ADVANCED TRIGONOMETRY, E. W. Hobson. Extraordinarily wide coverage, going beyond usual college level trig, one of the few works covering advanced trig in full detail. By a great expositor with unerring anticipation and lucid clarification of potentially difficult points. Includes circular functions; expansion of functions of multiple angle; trig tables; relations between sides and angles of triangle; complex numbers; etc. Many problems solved completely. "The best work on the subject." Nature. Formerly entitled "A Treatise on Plane Trigonometry." 689 examples. 6 figures. xvi + 383pp. 5⅜ x 8. **S353 Paperbound $1.95**

FAMOUS PROBLEMS OF ELEMENTARY GEOMETRY, Felix Klein. Expanded version of the 1894 Easter lectures at Göttingen. 3 problems of classical geometry, in an excellent mathematical treatment by a famous mathematician: squaring the circle, trisecting angle, doubling cube. Considered with full modern implications: transcendental numbers, pi, etc. Notes by R. Archibald. 16 figures. xi + 92pp. 5⅜ x 8. **T298 Paperbound $1.00**

MONOGRAPHS ON TOPICS OF MODERN MATHEMATICS, edited by J. W. A. Young. Advanced mathematics for persons who haven't gone beyond or have forgotten high school algebra. 9 monographs on foundation of geometry, modern pure geometry, non-Euclidean geometry, fundamental propositions of algebra, algebraic equations, functions, calculus, theory of numbers, etc. Each monograph gives proofs of important results, and descriptions of leading methods, to provide wide coverage. New introduction by Prof. M. Kline, N. Y. University. 100 diagrams. xvi + 416pp. 6⅛ x 9¼. **S289 Paperbound $2.00**

HIGHER MATHEMATICS FOR STUDENTS OF CHEMISTRY AND PHYSICS, J. W. Mellor. Not abstract, but practical, building its problems out of familiar laboratory material, this covers differential calculus, coordinate, analytical geometry, functions, integral calculus, infinite series, numerical equations, differential equations, Fourier's theorem, probability, theory of errors, calculus of variations, determinants. "If the reader is not familiar with this book, it will repay him to examine it," CHEM. & ENGINEERING NEWS. 800 problems. 189 figures. Bibliography. xxi + 641pp. 5⅜ x 8. **S193 Paperbound $2.25**

TRIGONOMETRY REFRESHER FOR TECHNICAL MEN, A. Albert Klaf. 913 detailed questions and answers cover the most important aspects of plane and spherical trigonometry. They will help you to brush up or to clear up difficulties in special areas. The first portion of this book covers plane trigonometry, including angles, quadrants, trigonometrical functions, graphical representation, interpolation, equations, logarithms, solution of triangle, use of the slide rule and similar topics. 188 pages then discuss application of plane trigonometry to special problems in navigation, surveying, elasticity, architecture, and various fields of engineering. Small angles, periodic functions, vectors, polar coordinates, de Moivre's theorem are fully examined. The third section of the book then discusses spherical trigonometry and the solution of spherical triangles, with their applications to terrestrial and astronomical problems. Methods of saving time with numerical calculations, simplification of principal functions of angle, much practical information make this a most useful book. 913 questions answered. 1738 problems, answers to odd numbers. 494 figures. 24 pages of useful formulae, functions. Index. x + 629pp. 5⅜ x 8. **T371 Paperbound $2.00**

TEXTBOOK OF ALGEBRA, G. Chrystal. One of the great mathematical textbooks, still about the best source for complete treatments of the topics of elementary algebra; a chief reference work for teachers and students of algebra in advanced high school and university courses, or for the mathematician working on problems of elementary algebra or looking for a background to more advanced topics. Ranges from basic laws and processes to extensive examination of such topics as limits, infinite series, general properties of integral numbers, and probability theory. Emphasis is on algebraic form, the foundation of analytical geometry and the key to modern developments in algebra. Prior course in algebra is desirable, but not absolutely necessary. Includes theory of quotients, distribution of products, arithmetical theory of surds, theory of interest, permutations and combinations, general expansion theorems, recurring fractions, and much, much more. Two volume set. Index in each volume. Over 1500 exercises, approximately half with answers. Total of xlviii + 1187pp. 5⅜ x 8. **S750 Vol I Paperbound $2.35** **S751 Vol II Paperbound $2.35** **The set $4.70**

MATHEMATICS—INTERMEDIATE TO ADVANCED

General

INTRODUCTION TO APPLIED MATHEMATICS, Francis D. Murnaghan. A practical and thoroughly sound introduction to a number of advanced branches of higher mathematics. Among the selected topics covered in detail are: vector and matrix analysis, partial and differential equations, integral equations, calculus of variations, Laplace transform theory, the vector triple product, linear vector functions, quadratic and bilinear forms, Fourier series, spherical harmonics, Bessel functions, the Heaviside expansion formula, and many others. Extremely useful book for graduate students in physics, engineering, chemistry, and mathematics. Index. 111 study exercises with answers. 41 illustrations. ix + .389pp. 5⅜ x 8½.
S1042 Paperbound **$2.00**

OPERATIONAL METHODS IN APPLIED MATHEMATICS, H. S. Carslaw and J. C. Jaeger. Explanation of the application of the Laplace Transformation to differential equations, a simple and effective substitute for more difficult and obscure operational methods. Of great practical value to engineers and to all workers in applied mathematics. Chapters on: Ordinary Linear Differential Equations with Constant Coefficients;; Electric Circuit Theory; Dynamical Applications; The Inversion Theorem for the Laplace Transformation; Conduction of Heat; Vibrations of Continuous Mechanical Systems; Hydrodynamics; Impulsive Functions; Chains of Differential Equations; and other related matters. 3 appendices. 153 problems, many with answers. 22 figures. xvi + 359pp. 5⅜ x 8½.
S1011 Paperbound **$2.25**

APPLIED MATHEMATICS FOR RADIO AND COMMUNICATIONS ENGINEERS, C. E. Smith. No extraneous material here!—only the theories, equations, and operations essential and immediately useful for radio work. Can be used as refresher, as handbook of applications and tables, or as full home-study course. Ranges from simplest arithmetic through calculus, series, and wave forms, hyperbolic trigonometry, simultaneous equations in mesh circuits, etc. Supplies applications right along with each math topic discussed. 22 useful tables of functions, formulas, logs, etc. Index. 166 exercises, 140 examples, all with answers. 95 diagrams. Bibliography. x + 336pp. 5⅜ x 8.
S141 Paperbound **$1.75**

Algebra, group theory, determinants, sets, matrix theory

ALGEBRAS AND THEIR ARITHMETICS, L. E. Dickson. Provides the foundation and background necessary to any advanced undergraduate or graduate student studying abstract algebra. Begins with elementary introduction to linear transformations, matrices, field of complex numbers; proceeds to order, basal units, modulus, quaternions, etc.; develops calculus of linears sets, describes various examples of algebras including invariant, difference, nilpotent, semi-simple. "Makes the reader marvel at his genius for clear and profound analysis," Amer. Mathematical Monthly. Index. xii + 241pp. 5⅜ x 8.
S616 Paperbound **$1.50**

THE THEORY OF EQUATIONS WITH AN INTRODUCTION TO THE THEORY OF BINARY ALGEBRAIC FORMS, W. S. Burnside and A. W. Panton. Extremely thorough and concrete discussion of the theory of equations, with extensive detailed treatment of many topics curtailed in later texts. Covers theory of algebraic equations, properties of polynomials, symmetric functions, derived functions, Horner's process, complex numbers and the complex variable, determinants and methods of elimination, invariant theory (nearly 100 pages), transformations, introduction to Galois theory, Abelian equations, and much more. Invaluable supplementary work for modern students and teachers. 759 examples and exercises. Index in each volume. Two volume set. Total of xxiv + 604pp. 5⅜ x 8.
S714 Vol I Paperbound **$1.85**
S715 Vol II Paperbound **$1.85**
The set **$3.70**

COMPUTATIONAL METHODS OF LINEAR ALGEBRA, V. N. Faddeeva, translated by C. D. Benster. First English translation of a unique and valuable work, the only work in English presenting a systematic exposition of the most important methods of linear algebra—classical and contemporary. Shows in detail how to derive numerical solutions of problems in mathematical physics which are frequently connected with those of linear algebra. Theory as well as individual practice. Part I surveys the mathematical background that is indispensable to what follows. Parts II and III, the conclusion, set forth the most important methods of solution, for both exact and iterative groups. One of the most outstanding and valuable features of this work is the 23 tables, double and triple checked for accuracy. These tables will not be found elsewhere. Author's preface. Translator's note. New bibliography and index. x + 252pp. 5⅜ x 8.
S424 Paperbound **$1.95**

ALGEBRAIC EQUATIONS, E. Dehn. Careful and complete presentation of Galois' theory of algebraic equations; theories of Lagrange and Galois developed in logical rather than historical form, with a more thorough exposition than in most modern books. Many concrete applications and fully-worked-out examples. Discusses basic theory (very clear exposition of the symmetric group); isomorphic, transitive, and Abelian groups; applications of Lagrange's and Galois' theories; and much more. Newly revised by the author. Index. List of Theorems. xi + 208pp. 5⅜ x 8.
S697 Paperbound **$1.45**

Catalogue of Dover Books

ALGEBRAIC THEORIES, L. E. Dickson. Best thorough introduction to classical topics in higher algebra develops theories centering around matrices, invariants, groups. Higher algebra, Galois theory, finite linear groups, Klein's icosahedron, algebraic invariants, linear transformations, elementary divisors, invariant factors; quadratic, bi-linear, Hermitian forms, singly and in pairs. Proofs rigorous, detailed; topics developed lucidly, in close connection with their most frequent mathematical applications. Formerly "Modern Algebraic Theories." 155 problems. Bibliography. 2 indexes. 285pp. 5⅜ x 8. S547 Paperbound **$1.50**

LECTURES ON THE ICOSAHEDRON AND THE SOLUTION OF EQUATIONS OF THE FIFTH DEGREE, Felix Klein. The solution of quintics in terms of rotation of a regular icosahedron around its axes of symmetry. A classic & indispensable source for those interested in higher algebra, geometry, crystallography. Considerable explanatory material included. 230 footnotes, mostly bibliographic. 2nd edition, xvi + 289pp. 5⅜ x 8. S314 Paperbound **$1.85**

LINEAR GROUPS, WITH AN EXPOSITION OF THE GALOIS FIELD THEORY, L. E. Dickson. The classic exposition of the theory of groups, well within the range of the graduate student. Part I contains the most extensive and thorough presentation of the theory of Galois Fields available, with a wealth of examples and theorems. Part II is a full discussion of linear groups of finite order. Much material in this work is based on Dickson's own contributions. Also includes expositions of Jordan, Lie, Abel, Betti-Mathieu, Hermite, etc. "A milestone in the development of modern algebra," W. Magnus, in his historical introduction to this edition. Index. xv + 312pp. 5⅜ x 8. S482 Paperbound **$1.95**

INTRODUCTION TO THE THEORY OF GROUPS OF FINITE ORDER, R. Carmichael. Examines fundamental theorems and their application. Beginning with sets, systems, permutations, etc., it progresses in easy stages through important types of groups: Abelian, prime power, permutation, etc. Except 1 chapter where matrices are desirable, no higher math needed. 783 exercises, problems. Index. xvi + 447pp. 5⅜ x 8. S300 Paperbound **$2.25**

THEORY OF GROUPS OF FINITE ORDER, W. Burnside. First published some 40 years ago, this is still one of the clearest introductory texts. Partial contents: permutations, groups independent of representation, composition series of a group, isomorphism of a group with itself, Abelian groups, prime power groups, permutation groups, invariants of groups of linear substitution, graphical representation, etc. 45pp. of notes. Indexes. xxiv + 512pp. 5⅜ x 8. S38 Paperbound **$2.45**

CONTINUOUS GROUPS OF TRANSFORMATIONS, L. P. Eisenhart. Intensive study of the theory and geometrical applications of continuous groups of transformations; a standard work on the subject, called forth by the revolution in physics in the 1920's. Covers tensor analysis, Riemannian geometry, canonical parameters, transitivity, imprimitivity, differential invariants, the algebra of constants of structure, differential geometry, contact transformations, etc. "Likely to remain one of the standard works on the subject for many years . . . principal theorems are proved clearly and concisely, and the arrangement of the whole is coherent," MATHEMATICAL GAZETTE. Index. 72-item bibliography. 185 exercises. ix + 301pp. 5⅜ x 8. S781 Paperbound **$1.85**

THE THEORY OF GROUPS AND QUANTUM MECHANICS, H. Weyl. Discussions of Schroedinger's wave equation, de Broglie's waves of a particle, Jordan-Hoelder theorem, Lie's continuous groups of transformations, Pauli exclusion principle, quantization of Maxwell-Dirac field equations, etc. Unitary geometry, quantum theory, groups, application of groups to quantum mechanics, symmetry permutation group, algebra of symmetric transformation, etc. 2nd revised edition. Bibliography. Index. xxii + 422pp. 5⅜ x 8. S269 Paperbound **$2.25**

APPLIED GROUP-THEORETIC AND MATRIX METHODS, Bryan Higman. The first systematic treatment of group and matrix theory for the physical scientist. Contains a comprehensive, easily-followed exposition of the basic ideas of group theory (realized through matrices) and its applications in the various areas of physics and chem.stry: tensor analysis, relativity, quantum theory, molecular structure and spectra, and Eddington's quantum relativity. Includes rigorous proofs available only in works of a far more advanced character. 34 figures, numerous tables. Bibliography. Index. xiii + 454pp. 5⅜ x 8⅜. S1147 Paperbound **$2.50**

THE THEORY OF GROUP REPRESENTATIONS, Francis D. Murnaghan. A comprehensive introduction to the theory of group representations. Particular attention is devoted to those groups—mainly the symmetric and rotation groups—which have proved to be of fundamental significance for quantum mechanics (esp. nuclear physics). Also a valuable contribution to the literature on matrices, since the usual representations of groups are groups of matrices. Covers the theory of group integration (as developed by Schur and Weyl), the theory of 2-valued or spin representations, the representations of the symmetric group, the crystallographic groups, the Lorentz group, reducibility (Schur's lemma, Burnside's Theorem, etc.), the alternating group, linear groups, the orthogonal group, etc. Index. List of references. xi + 369pp. 5⅜ x 8½. S1112 Paperbound **$2.35**

THEORY OF SETS, E. Kamke. Clearest, amplest introduction in English, well suited for independent study. Subdivision of main theory, such as theory of sets of points, are discussed, but emphasis is on general theory. Partial contents: rudiments of set theory, arbitrary sets and their cardinal numbers, ordered sets and their order types, well-ordered sets and their cardinal numbers. Bibliography. Key to symbols. Index. vii + 144pp. 5⅜ x 8. S141 Paperbound **$1.35**

THEORY AND APPLICATIONS OF FINITE GROUPS, G. A. Miller, H. F. Blichfeldt, L. E. Dickson.
Unusually accurate and authoritative work, each section prepared by a leading specialist: Miller on substitution and abstract groups, Blichfeldt on finite groups of linear homogeneous transformations, Dickson on applications of finite groups. Unlike more modern works, this gives the concrete basis from which abstract group theory arose. Includes Abelian groups, prime-power groups, isomorphisms, matrix forms of linear transformations, Sylow groups, Galois' theory of algebraic equations, duplication of a cube, trisection of an angle, etc. 2 Indexes. 267 problems. xvii + 390pp. 5⅜ x 8. S216 Paperbound **$2.00**

THE THEORY OF DETERMINANTS, MATRICES, AND INVARIANTS, H. W. Turnbull. Important study includes all salient features and major theories. 7 chapters on determinants and matrices cover fundamental properties, Laplace identities, multiplication, linear equations, rank and differentiation, etc. Sections on invariants gives general properties, symbolic and direct methods of reduction, binary and polar forms, general linear transformation, first fundamental theorem, multilinear forms. Following chapters study development and proof of Hilbert's Basis Theorem, Gordan-Hilbert Finiteness Theorem, Clebsch's Theorem, and include discussions of apolarity, canonical forms, geometrical interpretations of algebraic forms, complete system of the general quadric, etc. New preface and appendix. Bibliography. xviii + 374pp. 5⅜ x 8. S699 Paperbound **$2.25**

AN INTRODUCTION TO THE THEORY OF CANONICAL MATRICES, H. W. Turnbull and A. C. Aitken. All principal aspects of the theory of canonical matrices, from definitions and fundamental properties of matrices to the practical applications of their reduction to canonical form. Beginning with matrix multiplications, reciprocals, and partitioned matrices, the authors go on to elementary transformations and bilinear and quadratic forms. Also covers such topics as a rational canonical form for the collineatory group, congruent and conjunctive transformation for quadratic and hermitian forms, unitary and orthogonal transformations, canonical reduction of pencils of matrices, etc. Index. Appendix. Historical notes at chapter ends. Bibliographies. 275 problems. xiv + 200pp. 5⅜ x 8. S177 Paperbound **$1.55**

A TREATISE ON THE THEORY OF DETERMINANTS, T. Muir. Unequalled as an exhaustive compilation of nearly all the known facts about determinants up to the early 1930's. Covers notation and general properties, row and column transformation, symmetry, compound determinants, adjugates, rectangular arrays and matrices, linear dependence, gradients, Jacobians, Hessians, Wronskians, and much more. Invaluable for libraries of industrial and research organizations as well as for student, teacher, and mathematician; very useful in the field of computing machines. Revised and enlarged by W. H. Metzler. Index. 485 problems and scores of numerical examples. iv + 766pp. 5⅜ x 8. S670 Paperbound **$3.00**

THEORY OF DETERMINANTS IN THE HISTORICAL ORDER OF DEVELOPMENT, Sir Thomas Muir. Unabridged reprinting of this complete study of 1,859 papers on determinant theory written between 1693 and 1900. Most important and original sections reproduced, valuable commentary on each. No other work is necessary for determinant research: all types are covered—each subdivision of the theory treated separately; all papers dealing with each type are covered; you are told exactly what each paper is about and how important its contribution is. Each result, theory, extension, or modification is assigned its own identifying numeral so that the full history may be more easily followed. Includes papers on determinants in general, determinants and linear equations, symmetric determinants, alternants, recurrents, determinants having invariant factors, and all other major types. "A model of what such histories ought to be," NATURE. "Mathematicians must ever be grateful to Sir Thomas for his monumental work," AMERICAN MATH MONTHLY. Four volumes bound as two. Indices. Bibliographies. Total of lxxxiv + 1977pp. 5⅜ x 8. S672-3 The set, Clothbound **$12.50**

Calculus and function theory, Fourier theory, infinite series, calculus of variations, real and complex functions

FIVE VOLUME "THEORY OF FUNCTIONS' SET BY KONRAD KNOPP

This five-volume set, prepared by Konrad Knopp, provides a complete and readily followed account of theory of functions. Proofs are given concisely, yet without sacrifice of completeness or rigor. These volumes are used as texts by such universities as M.I.T., University of Chicago, N. Y. City College, and many others. "Excellent introduction . . . remarkably readable, concise, clear, rigorous," JOURNAL OF THE AMERICAN STATISTICAL ASSOCIATION.

ELEMENTS OF THE THEORY OF FUNCTIONS, Konrad Knopp. This book provides the student with background for further volumes in this set, or texts on a similar level. Partial contents: foundations, system of complex numbers and the Gaussian plane of numbers, Riemann sphere of numbers, mapping by linear functions, normal forms, the logarithm, the cyclometric functions and binomial series. "Not only for the young student, but also for the student who knows all about what is in it," MATHEMATICAL JOURNAL. Bibliography. Index. 140pp. 5⅜ x 8. S154 Paperbound **$1.35**

THEORY OF FUNCTIONS, PART I, Konrad Knopp. With volume II, this book provides coverage of basic concepts and theorems. Partial contents: numbers and points, functions of a complex variable, integral of a continuous function, Cauchy's integral theorem, Cauchy's integral formulae, series with variable terms, expansion of analytic functions in power series, analytic continuation and complete definition of analytic functions, entire transcendental functions, Laurent expansion, types of singularities. Bibliography. Index. vii + 146pp. 5⅜ x 8. S156 Paperbound **$1.35**

CHEMISTRY AND PHYSICAL CHEMISTRY

ORGANIC CHEMISTRY, F. C. Whitmore. The entire subject of organic chemistry for the practicing chemist and the advanced student. Storehouse of facts, theories, processes found elsewhere only in specialized journals. Covers aliphatic compounds (500 pages on the properties and synthetic preparation of hydrocarbons, halides, proteins, ketones, etc.), alicyclic compounds, aromatic compounds, heterocyclic compounds, organophosphorus and organometallic compounds. Methods of synthetic preparation analyzed critically throughout. Includes much of biochemical interest. "The scope of this volume is astonishing," INDUSTRIAL AND ENGINEERING CHEMISTRY. 12,000-reference index. 2387-item bibliography. Total of x + 1005pp. 5⅜ x 8.
Two volume set.   S700 Vol I Paperbound **$2.00**
                                                              S701 Vol II Paperbound **$2.00**
                                                                              The set **$4.00**

THE MODERN THEORY OF MOLECULAR STRUCTURE, Bernard Pullman. A reasonably popular account of recent developments in atomic and molecular theory. Contents: The Wave Function and Wave Equations (history and bases of present theories of molecular structure); The Electronic Structure of Atoms (Description and classification of atomic wave functions, etc.); Diatomic Molecules; Non-Conjugated Polyatomic Molecules; Conjugated Polyatomic Molecules; The Structure of Complexes. Minimum of mathematical background needed. New translation by David Antin of "La Structure Moleculaire." Index. Bibliography. vii + 87pp. 5⅜ x 8½.   S987 Paperbound **$1.00**

CATALYSIS AND CATALYSTS, Marcel Prettre, Director, Research Institute on Catalysis. This brief book, translated into English for the first time, is the finest summary of the principal modern concepts, methods, and results of catalysis. Ideal introduction for beginning chemistry and physics students. Chapters: Basic Definitions of Catalysis (true catalysis and generalization of the concept of catalysis); The Scientific Bases of Catalysis (Catalysis and chemical thermodynamics, catalysis and chemical kinetics); Homogeneous Catalysis (acid-base catalysis, etc.); Chain Reactions; Contact Masses; Heterogeneous Catalysis (Mechanisms of contact catalyses, etc.); and Industrial Applications (acids and fertilizers, petroleum and petroleum chemistry, rubber, plastics, synthetic resins, and fibers). Translated by David Antin. Index. vi + 88pp. 5⅜ x 8½.   S998 Paperbound **$1.00**

POLAR MOLECULES, Pieter Debye. This work by Nobel laureate Debye offers a complete guide to fundamental electrostatic field relations, polarizability, molecular structure. Partial contents: electric intensity, displacement and force, polarization by orientation, molar polarization and molar refraction, halogen-hydrides, polar liquids, ionic saturation, dielectric constant, etc. Special chapter considers quantum theory. Indexed. 172pp. 5⅜ x 8.
                                                              S64 Paperbound **$1.50**

THE ELECTRONIC THEORY OF ACIDS AND BASES, W. F. Luder and Saverio Zuffanti. The first full systematic presentation of the electronic theory of acids and bases—treating the theory and its ramifications in an uncomplicated manner. Chapters: Historical Background; Atomic Orbitals and Valence; The Electronic Theory of Acids and Bases; Electrophilic and Electrodotic Reagents; Acidic and Basic Radicals; Neutralization; Titrations with Indicators; Displacement; Catalysis; Acid Catalysis; Base Catalysis; Alkoxides and Catalysts; Conclusion. Required reading for all chemists. Second revised (1961) eidtion, with additional examples and references. 3 figures. 9 tables. Index. Bibliography xii + 165pp. 5⅜ x 8.
                                                              S201 Paperbound **$1.50**

KINETIC THEORY OF LIQUIDS, J. Frenkel. Regarding the kinetic theory of liquids as a generalization and extension of the theory of solid bodies, this volume covers all types of arrangements of solids, thermal displacements of atoms, interstitial atoms and ions, orientational and rotational motion of molecules, and transition between states of matter. Mathematical theory is developed close to the physical subject matter. 216 bibliographical footnotes. 55 figures. xi + 485pp. 5⅜ x 8.   S95 Paperbound **$2.55**

THE PRINCIPLES OF ELECTROCHEMISTRY, D. A. MacInnes. Basic equations for almost every subfield of electrochemistry from first principles, referring at all times to the soundest and most recent theories and results; unusually useful as text or as reference. Covers coulometers and Faraday's Law, electrolytic conductance, the Debye-Hueckel method for the theoretical calculation of activity coefficients, concentration cells, standard electrode potentials, thermodynamic ionization constants, pH, potentiometric titrations, irreversible phenomena, Planck's equation, and much more. "Excellent treatise," AMERICAN CHEMICAL SOCIETY JOURNAL. "Highly recommended," CHEMICAL AND METALLURGICAL ENGINEERING. 2 Indices. Appendix. 585-item bibliography. 137 figures. 94 tables. ii + 478pp. 5⅝ x 8⅜.
                                                              S52 Paperbound **$2.45**

THE PHASE RULE AND ITS APPLICATION, Alexander Findlay. Covering chemical phenomena of 1, 2, 3, 4, and multiple component systems, this "standard work on the subject" (NATURE, London), has been completely revised and brought up to date by A. N. Campbell and N. O. Smith. Brand new material has been added on such matters as binary, tertiary liquid equilibria, solid solutions in ternary systems, quinary systems of salts and water. Completely revised to triangular coordinates in ternary systems, clarified graphic representation, solid models, etc. 9th revised edition. Author, subject indexes. 236 figures. 505 footnotes, mostly bibliographic. xii + 494pp. 5⅜ x 8.   S91 Paperbound **$2.45**

THE SOLUBILITY OF NONELECTROLYTES, Joel H. Hildebrand and Robert L. Scott. The standard work on the subject; still indispensable as a reference source and for classroom work. Partial contents: The Ideal Solution (including Raoult's Law and Henry's Law, etc.); Nonideal Solutions; Intermolecular Forces; The Liquid State; Entropy of Athermal Mixing; Heat of Mixing; Polarity; Hydrogen Bonding; Specific Interactions; "Solvation" and "Association"; Systems of Three or More Components; Vapor Pressure of Binary Liquid Solutions; Mixtures of Gases; Solubility of Gases in Liquids; of Liquids in Liquids; of Solids in Liquids; Evaluation of Solubility Parameters; and other topics. Corrected republication of third (revised) edition. Appendices. Indexes. 138 figures. 111 tables. 1 photograph. iv + 488pp. 5⅜ x 8½.
S1125 Paperbound **$2.50**

TERNARY SYSTEMS: INTRODUCTION TO THE THEORY OF THREE COMPONENT SYSTEMS, G. Masing. Furnishes detailed discussion of representative types of 3-components systems, both in solid models (particularly metallic alloys) and isothermal models. Discusses mechanical mixture without compounds and without solid solutions; unbroken solid solution series; solid solutions with solubility breaks in two binary systems; iron-silicon-aluminum alloys; allotropic forms of iron in ternary system; other topics. Bibliography. Index. 166 illustrations. 178pp. 5⅝ x 8⅜.
S631 Paperbound **$1.50**

THE KINETIC THEORY OF GASES, Leonard B. Loeb, University of California. Comprehensive text and reference book which presents full coverage of basic theory and the important experiments and developments in the field for the student and investigator. Partial contents: The Mechanical Picture of a Perfect Gas, The Mean Free Path—Clausius' Deductions, Distribution of Molecular Velocities, discussions of theory of the problem of specific heats, the contributions of kinetic theory to our knowledge of electrical and magnetic properties of molecules and its application to the conduction of electricity in gases. New 14-page preface to Dover edition by the author. Name, subject indexes. Six appendices. 570-item bibliography. xxxvi + 687pp. 5⅜ x 8½.
S942 Paperbound **$2.95**

IONS IN SOLUTION, Ronald W. Gurney. A thorough and readable introduction covering all the fundamental principles and experiments in the field, by an internationally-known authority. Contains discussions of solvation energy, atomic and molecular ions, lattice energy, transferral of ions, interionic forces, cells and half-cells, transference of electrons, exchange forces, hydrogen ions, the electro-chemical series, and many other related topics. Indispensable to advanced undergraduates and graduate students in electrochemistry. Index. 45 illustrations. 15 tables. vii + 206pp. 5⅜ x 8½.
S124 Paperbound **$1.50**

IONIC PROCESSES IN SOLUTION, Ronald W. Gurney. Lucid, comprehensive examination which brings together the approaches of electrochemistry, thermodynamics, statistical mechanics, electroacoustics, molecular physics, and quantum theory in the interpretation of the behavior of ionic solutions—the most important single work on the subject. More extensive and technical than the author's earlier work (IONS IN SOLUTION), it is a middle-level text for graduate students and researchers in electrochemistry. Covers such matters as Brownian motion in liquids, molecular ions in solution, heat of precipitation, entropy of solution, proton transfers, dissociation constant of nitric acid, viscosity of ionic solutions, etc. 78 illustrations. 47 tables. Name and subject index. ix + 275pp. 5⅜ x 8½.
S134 Paperbound **$1.75**

CRYSTALLOGRAPHIC DATA ON METAL AND ALLOY STRUCTURES, Compiled by A. Taylor and B. J. Kagle, Westinghouse Research Laboratories. Unique collection of the latest crystallographic data on alloys, compounds, and the elements, with lattice spacings expressed uniformly in absolute Angstrom units. Gathers together previously widely-scattered data from the Power Data File of the ATSM, structure reports, and the Landolt-Bornstein Tables, as well as from other original literature. 2300 different compounds listed in the first table. Alloys and Intermetallic Compounds, with much vital information on each. Also listings for nearly 700 Borides, Carbides, Hydrides, Oxides, Nitrides. Also all the necessary data on the crystal structure of 77 elements. vii + 263pp. 5⅜ x 8.
S1013 Paperbound **$2.25**

MATHEMATICAL CRYSTALLOGRAPHY AND THE THEORY OF GROUPS OF MOVEMENTS, Harold Hilton. Classic account of the mathematical theory of crystallography, particularly the geometrical theory of crystal-structure based on the work of Bravais, Jordan, Sohncke, Federow, Schoenflies, and Barlow. Partial contents: The Stereographic Projection, Properties Common to Symmetrical and Asymmetrical Crystals, The Theory of Groups, Coordinates of Equivalent Points, Crystallographic Axes and Axial Ratios, The Forms and Growth of Crystals, Lattices and Translations, The Structure-Theory, Infinite Groups of Movements, Triclinic and Monoclinic Groups, Orthorhombic Groups, etc. Index. 188 figures. xii + 262pp. 5⅜ x 8½.
S1058 Paperbound **$2.00**

CLASSICS IN THE THEORY OF CHEMICAL COMBINATIONS. Edited by O. T. Benfey. Vol. I of the Classics of Science Series, G. Holton, Harvard University, General Editor. This book is a collection of papers representing the major chapters in the development of the valence concept in chemistry. Includes essays by Wöhler and Liebig, Laurent, Williamson, Frankland, Kekulé and Couper, and two by van't Hoff and le Bel, which mark the first extension of the valence concept beyond its purely numerical character. Introduction and epilogue by Prof. Benfey. Index. 9 illustrations. New translation of Kekulé paper by Benfey. xiv + 191pp. 5⅜ x 8½.
S1066 Paperbound **$1.85**

THE CHEMISTRY OF URANIUM: THE ELEMENT, ITS BINARY AND RELATED COMPOUNDS, J. J. Katz and E. Rabinowitch. Vast post-World War II collection and correlation of thousands of AEC reports and published papers in a useful and easily accessible form, still the most complete and up-to-date compilation. Treats "dry uranium chemistry," occurrences, preparation, properties, simple compounds, isotopic composition, extraction from ores, spectra, alloys, etc. Much material available only here. Index. Thousands of evaluated bibliographical references. 324 tables, charts, figures. xxi + 609pp. 5⅜ x 8.   S757 Paperbound **$2.95**

THE STORY OF ALCHEMY AND EARLY CHEMISTRY, J. M. Stillman. An authoritative, scholarly work, highly readable, of development of chemical knowledge from 4000 B.C. to downfall of phlogiston theory in late 18th century. Every important figure, many quotations. Brings alive curious, almost incredible history of alchemical beliefs, practices, writings of Arabian Prince Oneeyade, Vincent of Beauvais, Geber, Zosimos, Paracelsus, Vitruvius, scores more. Studies work, thought of Black, Cavendish, Priestley, Van Helmont, Bergman, Lavoisier, Newton, etc. Index. Bibliography. 579pp. 5⅜ x 8.   S628 Paperbound **$2.45**

Prices subject to change without notice.

Dover publishes books on art, music, philosophy, literature, languages, history, social sciences, psychology, handcrafts, orientalia, puzzles and entertainments, chess, pets and gardens, books explaining science, intermediate and higher mathematics, mathematical physics, engineering, biological sciences, earth sciences, classics of science, etc. Write to:

Dept. catrr.
Dover Publications, Inc.
180 Varick Street, N.Y. 14, N.Y.

73887

DATE DUE